Theodore R. Running

THE

THEORY OF ERRORS

AND

METHOD OF LEAST SQUARES

BY

WILLIAM WOOLSEY JOHNSON

PROFESSOR OF MATHEMATICS AT THE UNITED STATES NAVAL ACADEMY
ANNAPOLIS MARYLAND

FIRST EDITION

SECOND THOUSAND

NEW YORK:
JOHN WILEY & SONS.
LONDON: CHAPMAN & HALL, LIMITED.
1909

The Scientific Press
Robert Drummond and Company
New York

PREFACE.

THE basis adopted in this book for the theory of accidental errors is that laid down by Gauss in the *Theoria Motus Corporum Cœlestium* (republished as vol. vii of the *Werke*), which may be described for the most part in his own words, as follows :

"The hypothesis is in fact wont to be considered as an axiom that, if any quantity has been determined by several direct observations, made under similar circumstances and with equal care, the arithmetical mean between all the observed values presents the most probable value, if not with absolute rigor, at least very nearly so, so that it is always safest to adhere to it." (Art. 177.)

Then introducing the notion of a law of facility of error to give precise meaning to the phrase "most probable value," we cannot do better than to adopt that law of facility in accordance with which the arithmetical mean is the most probable value. After deriving this law and showing that it leads to the principle of least squares, he says : "This principle, which in all applications of mathematics to natural philosophy admits of very frequent use, ought everywhere to hold good as an axiom by the same right as that by which the arithmetical mean between several observed values of the same quantity is adopted as the most probable value." (Art. 179.)

43794

Accordingly no attempt has been made to demonstrate the principle of the arithmetical mean, nor to establish the exponential law of facility by any independent method. It has been deemed important, however, to show the self-consistent nature of the law, in the fact that its assumption for the errors of direct observation involves as a consequence a law of the same form for any linear function of observed quantities, and particularly for the final determination which results from our method. This persistence in the form of the law has too frequently been assumed, in order to simplify the demonstrations ; but at the expense of soundness.

No place has been given to the so-called criteria for the rejection of doubtful observations. Any doubt which attaches to an observation on account of the circumstances under which it is made, is recognized, in the practice of skilled observers, in its rejection, or in assigning it a small weight at the time it is made ; but these criteria profess to justify the subsequent rejection of an observation on the ground that its residual is found to exceed a certain limit. With respect to this Professor Asaph Hall says: " When observations have been honestly made I dislike to enter upon the process of culling them. By rejecting the large residuals the work is made to appear more accurate than it really is, and thus we fail to get the right estimate of its quality." (*The Orbit of Iapetus*, p. 40, *Washington Observations for* 1882, *Appendix I.*)

The notion that we are entitled to reject an observation, that is, to give it no weight, when its residual exceeds a certain limit, would seem to imply that we ought to give less than the usual weight to those observations whose residuals fall just short of this limit, in tact that we ought to revise the observations, assigning weights which diminish as the residuals increase. Such a process might appear at first sight plausible, but it would be equivalent to a complete departure from the principle of the arithmetical mean and the adoption of a new law of facility. For this we have no justification, either from theory or from the examination of the errors of extended sets of observations.

In the discussion of Gauss's method of solving the normal equations, the notion of the 'reduced observation equations' (see Arts. 154, 155) which gives a new interpretation to the 'reduced normal equations' has been introduced with advantage. This conception, although implied in Gauss's elegant discussion of the sum of the squares of the errors (see Art. 160), seems not to have appeared explicitly in any treatise prior to the third edition of W. Jordan's *Handbuch der Vermessungskunde* (Stuttgart, 1888). To this very complete work, and to Oppolzer's *Lehrbuch zur Bahnbestimmung der Kometen und Planeten*, I am indebted for the forms recommended for the computations connected with Gauss's method, and for many of the examples.

W. W. J.

U. S. Naval Academy, June, 1892.

CONTENTS.

I.

INTRODUCTORY.

II.

INDEPENDENT OBSERVATIONS OF A SINGLE QUANTITY.

III.

PRINCIPLES OF PROBABILITY.

IV.

THE LAW OF PROBABILITY OF ACCIDENTAL ERRORS.

V.

The Combination of Observations and Probable Accuracy of the Results.

VI.

The Facility of Error in a Function of one or more Observed Quantities.

VII.

The Combination of Independent Determinations of the same Quantity.

VIII.

Indirect Observations.

IX.

GAUSS'S METHOD OF SUBSTITUTION.

VALUES OF THE PROBABILITY INTEGRAL.

THE THEORY OF ERRORS AND METHOD OF LEAST SQUARES.

I.

INTRODUCTORY.

Errors of Observation.

1. A quantity of which the magnitude is to be determined is either directly measured, or, as in the more usual case, deduced by calculation from quantities which are directly measured. The result of a direct measurement is called an *observation*. Observations of the kind here considered are thus of the nature of readings upon some scale, generally attached to an instrument of observation. The *least count* of the instrument is the smallest difference recognized in the readings of the instrument, so that every observation is recorded as an integral multiple of the least count.

2. Repeated observations of the same quantity, even when made with the same instrument and apparently under the same circumstances, will nevertheless differ materially. An increase in the nicety of the observations, and the precision of the instrument, may decrease the discrepancies in actual magnitude; but at the same time, by diminishing the least count, their numerical measures will generally be increased; so that, with the most refined instruments, the discrepancies may amount to many times the least count. Thus every observation is subject to an *error*, the error being the difference between the observed value and the true value; an observed value which exceeds the true value is regarded as having a positive error, and one which falls short of it as having a negative error.

3. An error may be regarded as the algebraic sum of a number of elemental errors due to various causes. So far as these causes can be ascertained, their results are not errors at all, in the sense in which the term is here used, and are supposed to have been removed by means of proper corrections. *Systematic errors* are such as result from unknown causes affecting all the observations alike. These again are not the subjects of the "theory of errors," which is concerned solely with the *accidental errors* which produce the discrepancies between the observations.

Objects of the Theory.

4. It is obvious that when a set of repeated observations of the same quantity are made, the discrepancies between them enable us to judge of the degree of accuracy we have attained. Speaking in general terms, of two sets of observations, that is the best which exhibits upon the whole the smaller discrepancies. It is obvious also that from a set of observations we shall be able to obtain a result in which we can have greater confidence than in any single observation.

It is one of the objects of the theory of errors to deduce from a number of discordant observations (supposed to be already individually corrected, so far as possible) the best attainable result, together with a measure of its accuracy; that is to say, of the degree of confidence we are entitled to place in it.

5. When a number of unknown quantities are to be determined by means of equations involving observed quantities, the quantities sought are said to be *indirectly observed*. It is necessary to have as many such *observation equations* as there are unknown quantities. The case considered is that in which it is impossible to make repeated observations of the individual observed elements of the equations. These may, for example, be altitudes or other astronomical magnitudes which vary with the time, so that the corresponding times are also among the observed quantities. Nevertheless, there is the same advantage in employing a large number of observation equations that there is in the repetition of direct observations upon a single required quantity. If there are n unknown quantities, any group containing n of the equations would determine a set of values for the unknown quantities; but these values would differ from those given by any other group of n of the equations.

We may now state more generally the object of the theory of errors to be, when given more than n observation equations involving n unknown quantities, the equations being somewhat inconsistent, to derive from them the best determination of the values of the several unknown quantities, together with a measure of the degree of accuracy attained.

6. It will be noticed that, putting $n = 1$, this general statement includes the case of *direct observations*, in which all the equations are of the form

$$X = x_1, \quad X = x_2, \quad \ldots,$$

where X is the quantity to be determined, and each equation gives an independent statement of its value.

We commence with this case of direct observations of a single quantity, and our first consideration will be that of the best determination which can be obtained from a number of such observations.

II.

INDEPENDENT OBSERVATIONS OF A SINGLE QUANTITY.

The Arithmetical Mean.

7. Whatever rule we adopt for deducing the value to be accepted as the final result derived from several independent observations, it must obviously be such that when the observations are equal the result shall be the same as their common value. When the observations are discordant, such a rule produces an intermediate or *mean* value. Thus, if there be n quantities, $x_1, x_2, \ldots x_n$, the expressions

$$\frac{\Sigma x}{n}, \quad \sqrt[n]{(x_1 x_2 \ldots x_n)}, \quad \sqrt{\frac{\Sigma x^2}{n}}, \quad \text{etc.,}$$

give different sorts of mean values. Of these, the one first written, which is the *arithmetical mean*, is the simplest, and it is also that which has universally been accepted as the final value when $x_1, x_2, \ldots x_n$ are independently observed values of a single quantity x, the observations being all supposed equally good.

Residuals.

8. The differences between the several observed values and the value which we take as our final determination of the true value are called the *residuals* of the observations. The residuals are then what we take to be the errors of the observations; but they differ from them, of course, by the amount of error existing in our final determination. If the observed values were laid down upon a straight line, as measured from any origin, the residuals would be the abscissas of the points thus representing the observations when the point corresponding to the final value adopted is taken as the origin.

9. *In the case of the arithmetical mean, the algebraic sum of the residuals is zero.* For, if a denote the arithmetical mean of the n quantities $x_1, x_2, \ldots x_n$, we have

$$a = \frac{\Sigma x}{n}, \qquad \cdots \cdots \cdots \quad (1)$$

the residuals are

$$x_1 - a, \quad x_2 - a, \quad \ldots \quad x_n - a,$$

and their sum is

$$\Sigma x - na,$$

which is zero by equation (1).

When the observations are represented by points, as in the preceding article, the geometrical mean point or *centre of gravity* of these points is the point whose abscissa is a, and, when this point is taken as the origin, the sum of the positive abscissas of observation points is equal to the sum of the negative abscissas.

Weights.

10. When the observations are not made under the same circumstances, and are therefore not regarded as equally good, a greater relative importance can be given to a better observation by treating it as equivalent to more than one occurrence of the same observed value in a set of equally good observations. For example, if there were two observations giving the observed values x_1 and x_2, and the first observation were regarded as the best, we might proceed as if the observed value x_1 occurred twice and x_2 once in a set of three observations equally good. The arithmetical mean would then be

$$\frac{2x_1 + x_2}{3}.$$

In this process we are said to give to the observations the relative *weights* of 2 and 1. The weight may be regarded as the numerical measure of the influence of the observation upon the arithmetical mean.

11. In general, $p_1, p_2, \ldots p_n$ being taken as the weights of the observations $x_1, x_2, \ldots x_n$, the arithmetical mean with these weights is

$$a = \frac{p_1 x_1 + p_2 x_2 + \ldots + p_n x_n}{p_1 + p_2 + \ldots + p_n} = \frac{\Sigma p x}{\Sigma p}.$$

This expression is called the *weighted arithmetical mean.* When the weights are integers, it is the same as the arithmetical mean of Σp observations, of which p_1 give the observed value x_1, p_2 the observed value x_2, and so on. But, since only the ratios of the weights affect the result, it is not necessary to suppose them to be integers.

It is easily shown, as in Art. 9, that, if the residuals are multiplied by the weights, the algebraic sum of the results is zero. Again, when as in that article the observations are represented by points, the point whose abscissa is the weighted mean is the centre of gravity of bodies placed at the observation points having weights proportional to $p_1, p_2, \ldots p_n$.

12. The weight of a result obtained by the rule given above is defined to be the sum of the weights of its constituents; so that, because

$$a\Sigma p = \Sigma p x,$$

the product of a result by its weight is equal to the sum of the like products for its constituents. It follows that, in obtaining the final result, we may for any group of observations substitute their mean with the proper weight.

In the case of observations supposed equally good, the weight of each is taken equal to unity, and then the weight of the mean is the number of observations.

The Probable Value.

13. The *most probable value* of the observed quantity, or simply the *probable value*, in the ordinary sense of the expression signifies that which, in our actual state of knowledge, we are justified in considering as more likely than any other to be the true value. In this sense, the arithmetical mean is the most probable value which can be derived from observations considered equally good. This is, in fact, equivalent to saying that we accept the arithmetical mean as the best rule for combining the observations, having no reason either theoretical or practical for preferring any other.*

But, if instead of a rule of combination we adopt a theory with respect to the nature of accidental errors, the probable value will depend upon the adopted theory. To become the subject of mathematical treatment such a theory must take the shape of a law of the probability of accidental errors, as will be explained in a subsequent section. Since, in the nature of things, this law can never be absolutely known, and since moreover it probably differs with differing circumstances of observation, the most probable value in this technical sense is itself unknown. But when the expression is used without specifying the law of probability, it signifies the value which is the most probable in accordance with the generally accepted law of probability. Before proceeding to this law, we shall consider, in the following section, the principles of probability so far as we shall need to apply them.

Examples.

1. Show that the formula $nf(a) = \Sigma f(x)$ determines a mean value of n quantities for any form of the function f, and that the geometric mean is included in this rule.

2. Except when $f(x) = cx$ in Ex. 1, the position of the point whose abscissa is a is dependent upon the position of the origin as well as upon the observation points.

---

* That the most probable value, when there are but two observations, is their arithmetical mean follows rigorously from the hypothesis that positive and negative errors are equally probable. The property of the arithmetical mean pointed out in Art. 12 shows that the result for three observations is expressible as a function of the result for two of them and the third observation, and so on for four or more observations. It was upon the assumption that the most probable value must possess this property that Encke based his so-called proof that the arithmetical mean is the most probable value for any number of observations (*Berliner Astronomisches Jahrbuch* for 1834, pp. 260-262).

3. If the values of x are nearly equal in Ex. 1, the result of the formula is nearly equivalent to a weighted arithmetical mean in which the weights are proportional to $f'(\frac{1}{2}x_1 + \frac{1}{2}a)$, $f'(\frac{1}{2}x_2 + \frac{1}{2}a)$, etc.

4. When a mean value is determined by an equation of the form $\Sigma f(x - a) = 0$, the position of the point whose abscissa is a is independent of the origin. Give the cubic determining a when $\Sigma(x - a)^3 = 0$, and show that one root only is real.

5. Prove that the weighted arithmetical mean of values of $x + y$ is the sum of the like means of the values of x and of the values of y respectively.

III.

PRINCIPLES OF PROBABILITY.

The Measure of Probability.

14. The *probability* of a future event is the measure of our reasonable expectation of the event in our present state of knowledge of its causes. Thus, not knowing any reason to the contrary, when a die is to be thrown we assign an equal probability to the several events of the turning up of its six different faces. We say, therefore, that the probability or chance that the ace will turn up is 1 to 5, or better, 1 out of 6, hence the fraction $\frac{1}{6}$ is taken as the measure of the probability. Thus the probability of an event which is one of a set of equally likely events, one of which must happen, is the fraction whose numerator is unity and whose denominator is the number of these events. Obviously, *the probability of an event which can happen in several ways is the sum of the probabilities of the several ways.* Thus if the die had two blank faces, the probability that one of them would turn up would be $\frac{2}{6}$ or $\frac{1}{3}$. The sum of the probabilities of all the possible events is unity, which represents the certainty that some one of the events will happen.

Compound Events.

15. An event which consists of the joint occurrence of two independent events is called a *compound event*. By independent events we mean events such that the occurrence or non-occurrence of the first has no influence upon the occurrence or non-occurrence of the second. For example, the throwing of sixes with a pair of dice is a compound event consisting of the turning up of a special face of each die. The whole number of compound events is evidently the product of the numbers of simple events; and, since the several probabilities are the reciprocals of these numbers, the probability of the compound event is the product of the probabilities of the simple events. Thus, when a pair of dice is thrown we have $6 \times 6 = 36$ compound events, and the probability of a special one, such as the throwing of sixes, is $\frac{1}{6} \times \frac{1}{6} = \frac{1}{36}$.

In like manner, if more than two simple events are concerned, it is easily seen that, in general, *the probability of a compound event is the product of the probabilities of the independent simple events of whose joint occurrence it consists.*

16. A compound event may happen in different ways, and then, of course, the probabilities of these independent ways must be added. For example, six and five may be thrown in two ways, that is to say, two of the 36 equally likely events consist of the combination six and five, hence the chance is $\frac{2}{36}$ or $\frac{1}{18}$. A throw whose sum amounts to 10 can occur in three ways, therefore its chance is $\frac{3}{36}$ or $\frac{1}{12}$.

Repeated Trials.

17. When repeated opportunities for the occurrence or non-occurrence of the same set of events can be made to take place under exactly the same circumstances, equally probable events will tend to occur with the same frequency. Therefore, in a large number of such opportunities or *trials*, the relative frequency of the occurrence of an event which can happen in *m* ways and fail in *n* ways (the $m + n$ ways of both kinds corresponding to $m + n$ equally probable elementary events) will tend to the value $\dfrac{m}{m + n}$, which is the fraction expressing the probability of the event. This is commonly expressed by saying that the ratio of the number of occurrences of an event to the whole number of trials will "*in the long run*" be the fraction which expresses the probability. The correspondence of this frequency in the long run with the estimated probability forms the only mode, though an uncertain one, of submitting our results to the test of experience.

The Probability of Values belonging to a Continuous Series.

18. In the examples given in the preceding articles, the equally probable elementary events, which are the basis of our estimate of probability, form a limited number of distinct events, such as the turning up of the different faces of a die. But, in many applications, these events belong to a consecutive series, incapable of numeration. For example, suppose we are concerned with the value of a quantity x, of which it is known that any value between certain limits a and b is possible; or, what is the same thing, the position of the point P, whose abscissa is x, when P may have any position between certain extreme points A and B. We cannot now assign any finite measure to the probability that x shall have a definite value, or that P shall fall at a definite point, because the number of points upon the line AB is unlimited. We have rather to consider the probability that P shall fall upon a definite segment of the line, or that the value of x shall lie between certain limits.

19. It is customary, however, to compare the probabilities that P shall fall at certain points. Suppose in the first place

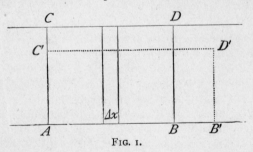

FIG. 1.

that, *when any equal segments of the line AB are taken, the probabilities that P shall fall in these segments are equal.* In this case, *the probability that P shall fall at a given point is said to be constant for all points of the line.* Let Δx be a segment of the line AB; then, if the probability for all points of AB is constant, it readily follows from the definition just given that the

probability that P shall fall in the segment $\varDelta x$ is proportional
to $\varDelta x$. Since we suppose it certain that P shall fall somewhere
between A and B, this probability will be represented by

$$\frac{\varDelta x}{AB} \quad \text{or} \quad \frac{\varDelta x}{b-a}.$$

Let an ordinate y be taken such that $y\varDelta x$ is the value of this
probability ; then

$$y = \frac{1}{b-a},$$

and, constructing as in Fig. 1 the line CD having this constant
ordinate, the probabilities for any segments of AB are the corresponding rectangles contained between the axis and the line
CD For different values of the limiting space AB in which P
may fall, y varies in inverse ratio. Thus, if AB is changed to
AB', the new ordinate AC' or y' is such that $y'.AB'=y.AB$,
each of the areas $ACDB$ and $AC'D'B'$ being equal to unity.
The two values of y are said to determine the relative probabilities that P shall fall at a given point in the two cases.

Curves of Probability.

20. Taking now the case in which the probability is not constant for all points, let AB be divided into segments, and let
rectangles be erected upon them, the area of each rectangle
representing the probability that P shall fall in the corresponding
segment.   The heights of these rectangles will now differ for the
different segments.   Denoting the height for a given segment
$\varDelta x$ by y, the relative values of y for any two segments determine, as explained in the preceding article, the relative probability that P shall fall at a given point in one or the other of the
segments, on the hypothesis that the probability is constant
throughout the segment.   They may thus be said to measure
the *mean values* of the probabilities for given points taken in the
various segments.   The sum of the areas of the rectangles will,
of course be unity ; that is, $\varSigma y\varDelta x = 1$.

21. If we now subdivide the segments, the figure composed of the sum of the rectangles will approach more and more nearly, as we diminish the segments without limit, to a curvilinear area, and the variable ordinate of the limiting curve will measure the continuously varying probability that P shall fall at a given point of the line AB.

The value of y is now a continuous function of x the abscissa of the corresponding point, and, putting $y = f(x)$, the function $f(x)$ is said to express the *law of the probability of the value x.*

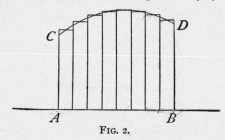

FIG. 2.

The curve $y = f(x)$ is the *probability curve* corresponding to the given law $f(x)$. The entire area $ACDB$, Fig. 2, whose value is $\int_a^b y\,dx$ (which is the limit of $\Sigma y \varDelta x$; see Int. Calc., Art. 99), a and b being the limiting values between which x certainly falls, is equal to unity. In general, for any limits the value of the integral $\int_a^\beta y\,dx$ is the probability that x falls between the values a and β. The element $y\,dx$ of this integral may be called the *element of probability* for the value x. It is sometimes called the probability that the value shall fall between x and $x + dx$, it being in that case understood that dx is taken so small that the probability may be regarded as constant in this interval.

22 As an illustration of what precedes, suppose it to be known that the value of x must fall between zero and a, and that the probabilities of values between these limits are proportional to the values themselves. These conditions give

$$y = cx,$$

and
$$\int_0^a y\,dx = 1,$$

whence, substituting and integrating,

$$\frac{ca^2}{2} = 1, \quad \text{or} \quad c = \frac{2}{a^2}.$$

Hence the law of probability in this case is

$$y = \frac{2x}{a^2}.$$

We may now find the probability that x shall fall between any given limits. For example, the probability that x shall exceed $\frac{1}{2}a$ is represented by

$$P = \int_{\frac{1}{2}a}^{a} y\,dx = \frac{2}{a^2} \int_{\frac{1}{2}a}^{a} x\,dx = \frac{3}{4}.$$

Thus the odds are 3 to 1 that x exceeds $\frac{1}{2}a$ when the law of probability is that proposed.

Mean Values under a given Law of Probability.

23. When a quantity x has a given law of probability, we have frequently occasion to consider what would be its *mean* or *average value* "in the long run," that is to say, the arithmetical mean of its values, supposing them to occur in a large number of trials with the frequency indicated by the given law of probability. See Art. 17.

Let us suppose, in the first place, that only a limited number of distinct values, say

$$x_1, x_2, \ldots x_m,$$

are possible. Let $P_1, P_2 \ldots P_m$ be the proper fractions which represent the respective probabilities of these values. Then, in a large number n of trials, the number of times in which the distinct values $x_1, x_2 \ldots x_m$ occur will be

$$nP_1, \ nP_2, \ldots nP_m$$

respectively. The arithmetical mean mentioned above is, therefore,

$$\frac{nP_1x_1 + nP_2x_2 + \ldots + nP_mx_m}{n};$$

that is, $P_1x_1 + P_2x_2 + \ldots + P_mx_m$,

or ΣPx.

That is to say, the mean value is found by multiplying the m distinct values by their probabilities and adding the results.*

24. Next, supposing a continuous series of values possible, let $y\varDelta x$ be taken, as in Art. 20, to represent the probability that x falls between x and $x + \varDelta x$. Evidently, in each term of ΣPx, we must now substitute this expression for P, and for x some intermediate value between x and $x + \varDelta x$. When we pass to the limit, in which y becomes a continuous function of x, this sum becomes

$$\int_a^b xy\,dx,$$

which is thus the mean value of x, when y is the function expressing its law of probability and a and b its extreme possible values.

For example, with the law of probability considered in Art. 22, namely,

$$y = \frac{2x}{a^2},$$

the mean value of x is

$$\frac{2}{a^2}\int_0^a x^2\,dx = \frac{2}{3}\,a.$$

25. In the same manner it may be shown that, if $y = f(x)$ expresses the law of probability of x, the mean value of any function $F(x)$ is

$$\int_a^b F(x)f(x)\,dx.$$

---

* The "value of an expectation" is an instance of a mean value. Thus, if x_1 is the value to be received in case a certain event whose probability is P_1 happens, x_2 the value to be received if an event whose probability is P_2 happens, and so on for m distinct events, one of which must happen, then the mean value ΣPx is called the value of the expectation.

Thus, again taking the law of probability $y = \dfrac{2x}{a^2}$, the mean value of x^2 * is

$$\frac{2}{a^2} \int_0^a x^3 dx = \frac{a^2}{2} .$$

Again, that of $\dfrac{1}{x}$ is

$$\frac{2}{a^2} \int_0^a dx = \frac{2}{a} .$$

26. If all values between a and b are equally probable, the element of probability is $\dfrac{dx}{b-a}$; thus the mean value of x, in this case, is

$$\int_a^b \frac{x \, dx}{b-a} = \frac{b^2 - a^2}{2(b-a)} = \frac{a+b}{2},$$

which is the same as the arithmetical mean between the limiting values. Again, the mean value of x^2, in this case, is

$$\int_a^b \frac{x^2 \, dx}{b-a} = \frac{b^3 - a^3}{3(b-a)} = \tfrac{1}{3}(b^2 + ab + a^2).$$

The Probability of Unknown Hypotheses.

27. No distinction can be drawn between the probability of an uncertain future event and that of an unknown contingency, in a case where the decisive "event" has indeed happened, but we remain in doubt with regard to it because only probable evidence

---

* It should be noticed that if $z = F(x)$, the law of probability for z is not found by simply expressing $f(x)$ as a function of z. It is necessary to transform the element of probability $f(x)dx$, which expresses the probability that x falls between x and $x + dx$, and therefore represents also the probability that z falls between z and $z + dz$. Thus, in the present case, putting $z = x^2$,

$$f(x)dx = \frac{2x}{a^2} \, dx = \frac{dz}{a^2},$$

which indicates that all values of z between 0 and a^2 are equally probable when, as supposed in Art. 22, the probability of a value of x is proportional to the value itself.

is known to us. In any case, the probability is a mental estimate of *credibility* depending only upon the known data, and therefore subject to change whenever new evidence becomes known. Let there be two hypotheses A and B, one of which must be true, and which so far as we know are equally probable, and suppose that a trial is to be made which on either hypothesis may eventuate in one or the other of two ways; in other words, that an event X may or may not happen. Suppose, further, that on the hypothesis A the probability of X is a, and on the hypothesis B the probability of X is b. Now it is clear that after the trial has been made and the event X has happened, we are entitled to make a different estimate of the relative credibilities of the hypotheses A and B.

28. To obtain the new measures of the probabilities of A and B, we employ the notion of relative frequency in the long run. Let us then consider a great number of cases of the four kinds which before the event X we regard as possible, the frequencies of the different kinds being proportional to their probabilities as we estimate them before the event. The hypotheses A and B respectively are true in an equal number of cases, say n, of each. The event X will happen in na of the cases in which A is true, and not happen in $n(1-a)$ cases. Again, X will happen in nb cases in which B is the true hypothesis, and not happen in $n(1-b)$ cases.

Now, since X has actually happened, from the whole number, $2n$, of cases we must exclude those in which X does not happen, and consider only the $na + nb$ cases in which X does happen.

Attending only to these cases, the relative frequency of those in which A and B respectively are true is the measure of our present estimate of their relative probability. Hence these probabilities are in the ratio $a:b$, that is, the probability of A is $\dfrac{a}{a+b}$, and that of B is $\dfrac{b}{a+b}$.

29. As an illustration, suppose there are two bags, A and B, containing white and black balls, A containing 3 white and 5 black balls, B containing 5 white and 1 black ball. One of the bags is chosen at random, and then a ball is drawn at random from the bag chosen. The ball is found to be white; what is the probability that the bag A was chosen? Here $a = \frac{3}{8}$, since three out of eight balls in A are white, and $b = \frac{5}{6}$; hence the probabilities are in the ratio $\frac{3}{8} : \frac{5}{6}$ or 9 : 20. The probability that the bag was A is therefore $\frac{9}{29}$.

Again, suppose A is known to contain only white balls, and B an equal number of white and black. If a white ball is drawn $a = 1$, $b = \frac{1}{2}$, the odds in favor of A are 2 : 1 or the probability of A is $\frac{2}{3}$. But if a black ball had been drawn, we should have had $a = 0$, $b = \frac{1}{2}$, the probability of A is zero, that is, it is certain that the bag chosen was not A.

30. If there are other hypotheses besides A and B consistent with the event X, the same reasoning as in Art. 28 establishes the general theorem that *the probabilities of the several hypotheses, which before an event X were considered equally probable,** are after the event proportional to the numbers which before the event express the probabilities of X on the several hypotheses.*

The various hypotheses in question may consist in attributing different values to an unknown quantity x, and these values may constitute a continuous series. The probabilities of the various values will then be proportional to the corresponding probabilities of the event X. Hence, to find the law of the probability of x, it is only necessary to determine a constant in the same manner that c is determined in Art. 22.

In particular it is to be noticed that, *of all the values of an unknown quantity which before the occurrence of a certain event were equally probable, that one is after the event the most probable which before the event assigned to it the greatest probability.*

---

* If this is not the case, the probabilities before the event are called the antecedent or *a priori* probabilities, and the theorem is that the ratio of the antecedent probabilities is to be multiplied by the probabilities of X on the several hypotheses, in order to find the ratio of the probabilities after the event.

Examples.

1. From $2n$ counters marked with consecutive numbers two are drawn at random; show that the odds against an even sum are n to $n-1$.

2. A and B play chess, A wins on an average 2 out of 3 games; what is the chance that A wins exactly 4 games out of the first six? $\frac{80}{243}$.

3. A domino is chosen from a set and a pair of dice is thrown; what is the chance that the numbers agree? $\frac{1}{28}$.

4. Show that the chance of throwing 9 with two dice is to the chance of throwing 9 with three dice as 24 to 25.

5. A and B shoot alternately at a mark. A hits once in n times, B once in $n-1$ times; show that their chances of first hit are equal, and find the odds in favor of B after A has missed the first shot. n to $n-2$.

6. A and B throw a pair of dice in turn. A wins if he throws numbers whose sum is 6 before B throws numbers whose sum is 7; show that his chance is $\frac{30}{61}$.

7. A walks at a rate known to be between 3 and 4 miles an hour. He starts to walk 20 miles, and B starts one hour later, walking at the rate of 4 miles an hour. What is the chance of overtaking him: 1° if all distances per hour between the limits are equally probable; 2° if all times per mile between the limits are equally probable?   1°, 1 to 2; 2°, 2 to 3.

8. If all values of x between 0 and a are possible and their probabilities are proportional to their squares, show that the probability that x exceeds $\frac{1}{2}a$ is $\frac{7}{8}$, and find the mean value of x. $\frac{3}{4}a$.

9. If, in the preceding example, we are informed that x exceeds $\frac{1}{2}a$, how is the probability affected, and what is now the mean value of x? $\frac{45}{56}a$.

10. If two points be taken at random upon a straight line AB, whose length is a, and X denote that which is nearest A, show that the curve of probability for X is a straight line passing through B, and find the mean value of AX. $\frac{1}{3}a$.

11. On a line AB, whose length is a, a point Z is taken at random, and then a point X is taken at random upon AZ. Determine the probability curve for AX, or x, and the mean value of x.

$$y = \frac{1}{a} \log \frac{a}{x} \; ; \; \frac{a}{4}.$$

12. Two points are taken at random on the circumference of a circle whose radius is a. Show that the chord is as likely as not to exceed $a\sqrt{2}$, but that the average length of the chord is $\frac{4a}{\pi}$.

13. In a semicircle whose radius is a, find the mean ordinate: 1° when all points of the semi-circumference are equally probable; 2° when all points on the diameter are equally probable.

$$1°, \; \frac{2a}{\pi} \; ; \; 2°, \; \frac{\pi a}{4}.$$

14. A card is missing from a pack; 13 cards are drawn at random and found to be black. Show that it is 2 to 1 that the missing card is red.

15. A card has been dropped from a pack; 13 cards are then drawn and found to be 2 spades, 3 clubs, 4 hearts, and 4 diamonds. What are the relative probabilities that the missing card belongs to the suits in the order named?   11 : 10 : 9 : 9.

16. A and B play at chess: when A has the first move the odds are 11 to 6 in favor of A, but when B has the first move the odds are only 9 to 5. A has won a game; what are the odds that he had the first move?   154 to 153.

17. The odds are 2 to 1 that a man will write 'rigorous' rather than 'rigourous.' The word has been written, and a letter taken at random from it is found to be 'u'; what are now the odds?   9 to 8.

18. A point P was taken at random upon a line AB, and then a point C was taken at random upon AP. If we are informed that C is the middle point of AB, what is now the probability curve of AP?

$$y = \frac{1}{x \log 2}.$$

IV.

THE LAW OF PROBABILITY OF ACCIDENTAL ERRORS.

The Facility of Errors.

31. If observations made upon the same magnitude could be repeated under the same circumstances indefinitely, only a limited number of observed values, which are exact multiples of the least count of the instrument, would occur, and the relative frequency with which they occurred would indicate the law of the probability of the observed values, that is to say, the *law of facility* with which the corresponding errors are committed. In the theory of errors, however, it is necessary to regard all observed values between certain limits as possible, so that when they are laid down upon a line as abscissas, the law of facility may be represented by a continuous curve, as explained in Art. 21. This is in fact equivalent to supposing the least count diminished without limit.

The curve thus obtained is the probability curve for an observed value; and, if the point representing the true value be taken as origin, the abscissas become errors, and the curve becomes the probability curve for accidental errors committed under the given circumstances.

32. The probability curves corresponding to different circumstances of observation would differ somewhat, but in any case would present the following general features. In the first place, since errors in defect and in excess* are equally likely to occur, the curve must be symmetrical to the right and left of the point which represents the true value of the observed quantity. In the next place, since accidental errors are made up of elemental errors (Art. 3) which, as they may have either direction, tend

---

* There is usually no distinction in kind between these : either direction may be taken as positive, and errors of a given magnitude in one direction or the other are equally likely to occur.

to cancel one another, small errors are more frequent than large ones, so that the maximum ordinate occurs at the central point. In the third place, since large errors (which can only result when most of the elemental errors have the same direction and their greatest magnitudes) are rare, and errors beyond some undefined limit do not occur, the curve must rapidly approach the axis of x both to the right and left, so that the ordinate (which can never become negative) practically vanishes at an indefinite distance from the central point.

33. If $y = \varphi(x)$ is the equation of the curve referred to the central point as origin, the general features mentioned above are equivalent to the statements: first, that $\varphi(x)$ is an even function, that is, a function of x^2; secondly, that $\varphi(0)$ is its maximum value; thirdly, that it is a decreasing function of x^2, and practically vanishes when x is large. Since it is impracticable to select the function φ in such a manner that $\varphi(x)$ shall be constantly equal to zero when x exceeds a certain limit, the last condition requires that the curve shall have the axis of x for an asymptote; in other words, we must have $\varphi(\pm \infty) = 0$.

When regarded as the curve of probability of an observed value, the equation is $y = \varphi(x - a)$, where a is the true value of the observed quantity, the origin now corresponding to the zero point of the measurements.

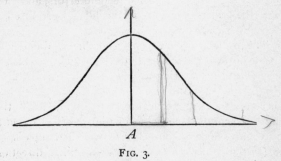

A

Fig. 3.

The general form of the curve of probability of an observed value will therefore be similar to that given in Fig. 3, in which A is the point whose abscissa a is the true value.

The Probability of an Error between given Limits.

34. If the law of probability of error for a given observation is

$$y = \varphi(x),$$

the probability that the error of an observation shall lie between a and β will, in accordance with Art. 21, be expressed by

$$P = \int_a^\beta \varphi(x)dx,$$

provided that the value of this integral for the whole range of possible errors is unity.   Since we suppose the function $\varphi(x)$ to fulfil the conditions given in Art. 32, we may include all errors in the range of the integral, because the probability of large errors practically vanishes.   We therefore write

$$\int_{-\infty}^{\infty} \varphi(x)dx = 1.$$

That is to say, the whole area between the curve and the axis in Fig. 3 is assumed to be unity.

35. If $\varDelta x$ represents the least count of the instrument, the probability that an observation shall be recorded with the value x will be represented by

$$\int_{x-\frac{1}{2}\varDelta x}^{x+\frac{1}{2}\varDelta x} \varphi(x)dx.$$

If $\varDelta x$ is so small that $\varphi(x)$ may be regarded as constant over the interval, the value of this integral is

$$\varphi(x)\varDelta x.$$

The product $\varphi(x)dx$, which is the *element of probability*, being the element of the area which represents the probability, is therefore called the probability of an error between x and $x + dx$, and is sometimes written in the form

$$\int_x^{x+dx} \varphi(x)dx.$$

The Probability of a System of Observed Values.

36. Let x_1, x_2, ... x_n be a series of observed values of a quantity whose true value is a, the observations being all made under the same circumstances. Then

$$x_1 - a, \quad x_2 - a, \quad \ldots \quad x_n - a$$

are the errors of observation; and,

$$y = \varphi(x - a) \quad \ldots \quad \ldots \quad (1)$$

being the law of facility of the errors, the probability before the first observation is made that x_1 shall be the first observed value is $\varphi(x_1 - a)\Delta x$, where Δx is the least count of the instrument. In like manner, the probability that x_2 shall be the second observed value is $\varphi(x_2 - a)\Delta x$, and so on.

It follows, in accordance with the principle explained in Art. 15, that, if P denote the probability of the compound event consisting in the occurrence of the n observed values, then, before the observations were made we should have

$$P = \varphi(x_1 - a) \, \varphi(x_2 - a) \ldots \varphi(x_n - a) \, \Delta x^n. \quad . \quad (2)$$

The Most Probable Value derivable from a given System of Observed Values.

37. Supposing the form of the function φ to be known, the value of P given above is a known function of the unknown true value a. Regarding different values of a as hypotheses all equally probable before the observations were made, the principle enunciated in Art. 30 shows that that value of a is most probable which assigns to P the greatest value.

The value of a thus found, or most probable value, depends therefore in part upon the form of the function φ, this being the mathematical expression of a law which, as stated in Art. 13, can never be absolutely known. We proceed to the method of Gauss, which consists in determining the form of φ in accordance with which the arithmetical mean becomes the most probable value.

The Form of φ corresponding to the Arithmetical Mean.

38. If we put

$$\log \varphi(x - a) = \psi(x - a), \quad \dots \quad (1)$$

we have from equation (2), Art. 36,

$$\log P = \psi(x_1 - a) + \psi(x_2 - a) + \ldots + \psi(x_n - a) + n \log \varDelta x, \quad (2)$$

and a is to be so taken that P, and therefore $\log P$, shall be a maximum. Hence, putting ψ' for the derivative of ψ, we have by differentiation with respect to a,

$$\psi'(x_1 - a) + \psi'(x_2 - a) + \ldots + \psi'(x_n - a) = 0. \quad (3)$$

Denoting the quantities

$$x_1 - a, \quad x_2 - a, \quad \ldots \quad x_n - a,$$

which are the residuals, by $v_1, v_2, \ldots v_n$, this equation may be written

$$\psi'(v_1) + \psi'(v_2) + \ldots + \psi'(v_n) = 0. \quad \dots \quad (4)$$

Supposing now the value of a which satisfies equation (3) to be the arithmetical mean, we have by Art. 9,

$$v_1 + v_2 + \ldots + v_n = 0. \quad \dots \quad (5)$$

We wish therefore to find the form of the function ψ' such that equation (4) is satisfied by every set of values of $v_1, v_2, \ldots v_n$ which satisfy equation (5). For this purpose, suppose all the values of v except v_1 and v_2 to remain unchanged while equation (5) is still satisfied. The new values may then be denoted by $v_1 + k$ and $v_2 - k$, in which k is arbitrary. Substituting the new values in equation (4), the sum of the first two terms must remain unchanged since all of the other terms are unchanged; therefore,

$$\psi'(v_1 + k) + \psi'(v_2 - k) = \psi'(v_1) + \psi'(v_2);$$

whence

$$\frac{\psi'(v_1 + k) - \psi'(v_1)}{k} = \frac{\psi'(v_2) - \psi'(v_2 - k)}{k}. \quad \dots \quad (6)$$

When k is diminished without limit this becomes

$$\frac{d\psi'(v)}{dv}\bigg]_{v_1} = \frac{d\psi'(v)}{dv}\bigg]_{v_2};$$

hence, because v_1 and v_2 are independent, we infer that

$$\frac{d\psi'(v)}{dv} = c, \quad \ldots \ldots \ldots \quad (7)$$

where c is an unknown constant.

The integral of equation (7) is $\psi'(v) = cv + c'$: but, substituting in equation (4), we find $c' = 0$; hence

$$\psi'(v) = cv. \quad \ldots \ldots \ldots \quad (8)$$

Integrating again,

$$\psi(v) = \tfrac{1}{2}cv^2 + c'',$$

or, by equation (1),

$$\log \varphi(v) = - h^2v^2 + c'', \quad \ldots \ldots \quad (9)$$

in which we have written $- h^2$ for the constant $\tfrac{1}{2}c$, because we know from Art. 33 that $\varphi(v)$ is a decreasing function of v^2.

Finally, equation (9) gives

$$\varphi(v) = Ce^{-h^2v^2}, \quad \ldots \ldots \ldots \quad (10)$$

which is accordingly the law of facility of error which makes the arithmetical mean the most probable value.

The Determination of the Value of C.

39. The constants C and h which arise in the above process are not independent; for, x denoting the error as in Art. 34, we must have

$$\int_{-\infty}^{\infty} \varphi(x)dx = 1.$$

Substituting from equation (10) above, this gives

$$C \int_{-\infty}^{\infty} e^{-h^2x^2} dx = 1, \quad \ldots \ldots \ldots \quad (1)$$

by which the value of C in terms of h may be found.

A convenient mode of evaluating the definite integral involved in this equation results from the consideration of the solid included between the plane of xy and the surface generated by the revolution of the curve

$$z = e^{-h^2 x^2}$$

about the axis of z. Using polar coordinates in the plane of xy, the equation of the surface is

$$z = e^{-h^2 r^2} = e^{-h^2 (x^2 + y^2)}. \qquad \dots \dots \quad (2)$$

The volume of the solid in question is therefore expressed by either of the two formulae

$$V = \int_{-\infty}^{\infty} \int_{-\infty}^{\infty} e^{-h^2 x^2} e^{-h^2 y^2} dx dy, \qquad \dots \dots \quad (3)$$

and

$$V = \int_{0}^{2\pi} \int_{0}^{\infty} e^{-h^2 r^2} r dr d\theta. \qquad \dots \dots \quad (4)$$

The second expression is readily evaluated and gives

$$V = \frac{\pi}{h^2} e^{-h^2 r^2} \Big]_{\infty}^{0} = \frac{\pi}{h^2}. \qquad \dots \dots \quad (5)$$

In equation (3), the limits of integration are independent; hence

$$V = \int_{-\infty}^{\infty} e^{-h^2 x^2} dx \cdot \int_{-\infty}^{\infty} e^{-h^2 y^2} dy = \left[\int_{-\infty}^{\infty} e^{-h^2 x^2} dx \right]^2. \quad (6)$$

Comparing equations (5) and (6), we have

$$\int_{-\infty}^{\infty} e^{-h^2 x^2} dx = \frac{\sqrt{\pi}}{h}.* \qquad \dots \dots \quad (7)$$

Substituting in equation (1), we have $C = \dfrac{h}{\sqrt{\pi}}$, and the law of facility becomes

$$y = \frac{h}{\sqrt{\pi}} e^{-h^2 x^2}, \qquad \dots \dots \quad (8)$$

---

* It is readily shown that $\int_{-\infty}^{\infty} e^{-t^2} dt = \Gamma(\tfrac{1}{2})$, the value of which is $\sqrt{\pi}$: equation (7) may also be derived by putting $t = hx$ in this result.

ich, it is readily seen, fulfils the conditions given in

40. The law of facility expressed in the equation derived above is that which is universally adopted ; in other words, it is assumed that under any circumstances of observation the law of facility will be satisfactorily represented by equation (8) if the value of *h* be properly determined. The mode of determining the most probable value of *h* for a given set of observations will be given in the following section.

We proceed to develop the consequences of this law. Among them will, of course, be found the rule of the Arithmetical Mean in accordance with which the law has been derived (see Art. 42). Certain confirmations of the law, both of a theoretic and a practical nature, will also be noticed as they present themselves.

The Principle of Least Squares.

41. Substituting the expression now obtained for the function φ, the expression for the probability of the occurrence of the actual observed values (as estimated before the observations were made, see Art. 36) becomes

$$P = \frac{h^n}{\pi^{\frac{1}{2}n}} e^{-h^2[(x_1-a)^2 + (x_2-a)^2 + \cdots + (x_n-a)^2]} \varDelta x^n . \quad . \quad (1)$$

This expression, regarded as a function of *a*, is obviously a maximum when

$$(x_1 - a)^2 + (x_2 - a)^2 + \ldots + (x_n - a)^2 = \text{a minimum.} \quad (2)$$

Hence the most probable value of the observed quantity *a*, in the case of observations supposed equally good, is *that which assigns the least possible value to the sum of the squares of the residual errors*. This is the statement in its simplest form of *the principle of Least Squares*.

42. The rule of the Arithmetical Mean follows directly from the principle of Least Squares. Thus, by differentiation with respect to *a*, we derive from equation (2)

$$x_1 - a + x_2 - a + \ldots + x_n - a = 0;$$

that is, the algebraic sum of the residuals is zero, or

$$a = \frac{\Sigma x}{n};$$

in other words, the arithmetical mean is to be taken as the most probable value.

43. Conversely, we may show directly that the arithmetical mean makes the sum of the squares of the residuals a minimum. For, if a is the arithmetical mean, the residuals are

$$v_1 = x_1 - a, \quad v_2 = x_2 - a, \quad \ldots \quad v_n = x_n - a,$$

and $\Sigma v = 0$. Now if δ is the error of the arithmetical mean, the true value of the observed quantity is $a - \delta$, and the true expressions for the errors of the observed values are

$$x_1 - a + \delta = v_1 + \delta, \quad \ldots \quad x_n - a + \delta = v_n + \delta.$$

The sum of the squares of the n errors is therefore

$$\Sigma(v + \delta)^2 = \Sigma v^2 + 2\delta \Sigma v + n\delta^2$$
$$= \Sigma v^2 + n\delta^2,$$

since $\Sigma v = 0$. The minimum value of this expression is obviously Σv^2, the value assumed when $\delta = 0$; that is to say, the sum of the squares of the residuals is least when the arithmetical mean is taken as the value of the observed quantity.

The Probability Integral.

44. Taking now the probability curve to be

$$y = \frac{h}{\sqrt{\pi}} e^{-h^2 x^2}, \quad \ldots \quad \ldots \quad \text{(1)}$$

the probability of an error between a and β in magnitude is

$$\frac{h}{\sqrt{\pi}} \int_a^\beta e^{-h^2 x^2} dx,$$

and, in particular, the probability of an error numerically less than δ is

$$P = \frac{h}{\sqrt{\pi}} \int_{-\delta}^{\delta} e^{-h^2 x^2} dx. \quad \ldots \quad \ldots \quad \text{(2)}$$

If we put $hx = t$, this may be written in the form

$$P = \frac{1}{\sqrt{\pi}} \int_{-h\delta}^{h\delta} e^{-t^2} dt = \frac{2}{\sqrt{\pi}} \int_{0}^{h\delta} e^{-t^2} dt, \quad . \quad . \quad (3)$$

which shows that P depends solely upon the value of $h\delta$, that is, upon the limiting value of t.

Table I gives the values of this integral for values of t from 0 to 2 at intervals of .01. The halves of the tabular numbers are the values of the probability of an error whose reduced value falls between the limits 0 and t, and by combining these we can readily find the values of the probability for any given limits.

The Measure of Precision.

45. The value of h in the probability curve depends upon the circumstances of observation. Let h_1 and h_2 be the values of h corresponding to two sets of observations for which the curves

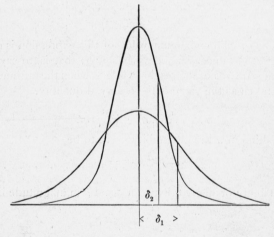

Fig. 4.

are drawn in Fig. 4. The ordinates corresponding to $x = 0$ in the two curves are proportional to the values of h. Hence, because small errors are relatively more frequent in the better set of observations, the value of h for this set will be the larger.

46. Let δ_1 be any error, and put

$$h_1\delta_1 = t = h_2\delta_2;$$

then, because δ_1 in the first set of observations and δ_2 in the second set correspond to the same value of t in the probability integral, equation (3), Art. 44, the probability that an error shall be less than δ_1 in the first set is the same as the probability that an error shall be less than δ_2 in the second set. In Fig. 4, for example, we have taken $h_2 = 2h_1$; it follows that $\delta_2 = \frac{1}{2}\delta_1$; that is to say, the probability that an error shall not exceed a given limit in the first case is the same as the probability that an error shall not exceed one half of the given limit in the second case.* The ordinates corresponding to δ_1 and δ_2 in the two curves are drawn in Fig. 4. The areas cut off in the two cases are equal. It is, in fact, readily seen that the second curve might have been derived from the first by reducing the abscissa of each point of the curve to one half its value and at the same time doubling the corresponding ordinate, a process which evidently would not affect the total area, which, as we have seen, must always be equal to unity.

47. The ratio of δ_1 and δ_2 which correspond to the same probability may be said to measure *the relative risk of error* in the two cases. Thus, in the example illustrated in Fig. 4, the risk of error in the first case is double that in the second case. It is natural to regard the precision of the observations in the second case as double that of the observations in the first case. So also, in general, the ratio of *precision* is inversely that of the *risk of error;* that is to say, it is the direct ratio of the values of h, which are inversely proportional to the corresponding values of δ. Accordingly h is taken as the *measure of precision.*

---

* This is frequently inaccurately expressed by the statement that the probability of a given error in the first case is the same as that of the half error in the second case.

If the errors in any system of observations are multiplied by the proper values of h, the results are the corresponding values of t. Errors belonging to different systems may thus be reduced to the same scale, and the values of t, or *reduced errors*, will then admit of direct comparison.

The Probable Error.

48. The error which is just as likely to be exceeded as not is called *the probable error*.* In other words, the probable error is the value of δ for which $P = \frac{1}{2}$ in equation (2), Art. 44. Denoting by ρ the corresponding value of t in equation (3) of the same article, we have

$$\frac{1}{2} = \frac{2}{\sqrt{\pi}} \int_0^\rho e^{-t^2} dt.$$

The solution of this equation has been found to be

$$\rho = 0.476936,$$

which is the value of t corresponding to the interpolated value $P = 0.5$ in Table I.

Denoting the probable error by r, we have then

$$rh = \rho,$$

$$r = \frac{\rho}{h} = \frac{0.4769}{h}.$$

The Mean Absolute Error.

49. The mean value of all possible errors, having regard to their probability or frequency in the long run, is, in accordance with Art. 24,

$$\frac{h}{\sqrt{\pi}} \int_{-\infty}^{\infty} x e^{-h^2 x^2} dx.$$

---

* The "probable error" is thus not the *most* probable error, which is, of course, the error zero, for which the ordinate of the probability curve is a maximum.

The value of this is of course zero, the parts of the integral corresponding to positive and negative errors being equal and having contrary signs. The value obtained by taking both parts of the integral as positive is the mean of the errors taken all positively, or *the mean of the absolute values of the errors.* Denoting this mean by η, we have

$$\eta = \frac{2h}{\sqrt{\pi}} \int_0^\infty x e^{-h^2 x^2} dx;$$

whence

$$\eta = \frac{1}{h\sqrt{\pi}}.$$

The Mean Error.

50. The mean of all values of the square of the error, having regard to their probabilities, is, in like manner (see Art. 25),

$$\frac{h}{\sqrt{\pi}} \int_{-\infty}^\infty x^2 e^{-h^2 x^2} dx.$$

The error whose square has this mean value is denoted by ε. On account of its importance in the theory, this error is called the *mean error*. Thus

$$\varepsilon^2 = \frac{h}{\sqrt{\pi}} \int_{-\infty}^\infty x^2 e^{-h^2 x^2} dx.$$

The value of the definite integral involved in this expression may be deduced from the result found in Art. 39, equation (7), namely,

$$\int_{-\infty}^\infty e^{-h^2 x^2} dx = \frac{\sqrt{\pi}}{h}.$$

Differentiating with respect to h, we have

$$-2h \int_{-\infty}^\infty x^2 e^{-h^2 x^2} dx = -\frac{\sqrt{\pi}}{h^2},$$

and, substituting in the value of ε^2, we find

$$\varepsilon^2 = \frac{1}{2h^2}, \quad \text{or} \quad \varepsilon = \frac{1}{h\sqrt{2}}.$$

Measures of the Risk of Error.

51. We have seen in Art. 47 that the errors corresponding in two different systems to the same value of the reduced error t measure by their ratio the comparative risk of error in the two systems. Thus the error corresponding to any fixed value of t might be taken as the measure of this risk. Accordingly either of the errors

$$r, \qquad \eta, \qquad \varepsilon,$$

which correspond respectively to the reduced errors

$$\rho, \qquad \frac{1}{\sqrt{\pi}}, \qquad \frac{1}{\sqrt{2}},$$

may be taken as *the measure of the risk of error** or *inverse measure of precision.*

The probable error r is that which is most frequently employed in practice. Each of the others bears a fixed ratio to r, their values being respectively

---

* The error η was called by De Morgan the *mean risk of error*, because it is the mean expectation of error, using the term expectation in the same sense as in the expression "value of an expectation." (See footnote on page 15.) It corresponds to what is generally called in annuity tables "the expectation of life" for persons of a given age, which should rather be called "the mean duration of survival" for persons of the given age. On the other hand, the probable error r is analogous to the remaining term for which a person of the given age is as likely as not to live. This might be called "the probable term of survival," and its value may differ materially from the mean duration. Thus, according to the Carlisle mortality table, one half of the whole number of persons thirty years old survive for the term of 36.6 years, but the mean duration of life for such persons, as computed from the same table, is only 34.3 years. This indicates that the law of mortality is such that the half which exceed the term of probable survival do so by a total amount less than that by which the other half fall short of it.

In the case of errors the difference falls in the opposite direction. In the long run one half of the errors exceed r; and the fact that $\eta > r$ shows that the half which exceed r do so by a total amount greater than that by which the other half fall short of it.

$$\eta = \frac{r}{\rho \sqrt{\pi}} = 1.1829\,r, \quad \cdots \quad (1)$$

$$\varepsilon = \frac{r}{\rho \sqrt{2}} = 1.4826\,r, \quad \cdots \quad (2)$$

52. Fig. 5 shows the positions of the ordinates corresponding to r, η and ε in the curve of facility of errors

$$y = \frac{h}{\sqrt{\pi}}\,e^{-h^2 x^2}.$$

The diagram is constructed for the value $h = 2$.

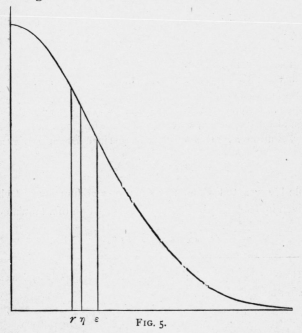

Fig. 5.

From the definitions of the errors it is evident that the ordinate of r bisects the area between the curve and the axes, that of η passes through its centre of gravity, and that of ε passes through its centre of gyration about the axis of y.

The advantage of employing in practice a measure of the risk of error, instead of the direct measure of precision, results from the fact that it is of the same nature and expressed in the same units as the observations themselves. It therefore conveys a better idea of the degree of accuracy than is given by the value of the abstract quantity h. When the latter is given, it is of course necessary also to know the unit used in expressing the errors.

Tables of the Probability Integral.

53. The integral $\int_0^t e^{-t^2} dt$ is known as *the error function* and is denoted by Erf t.* Table I, which has already been described, Art. 44, gives the values of $\dfrac{2}{\sqrt{\pi}}$ Erf t, which is the probability that an error shall be numerically less than the error x, of which the reduced value is t. The argument of this table is the reduced error t.

But it is convenient to have the values of the probability given also for values of the ratio of the error x to the probable error. Putting z for this ratio, we have, since $hx = t$ and $hr = \rho$,

$$z = \frac{x}{r} = \frac{t}{\rho}.$$

Table II gives, to the argument z, the same function of t which is given in Table I; that is to say, the function of z tabulated is

$$P_z = \frac{2}{\sqrt{\pi}} \text{ Erf } \rho z,$$

---

* The integral $\int_t^\infty e^{-t^2} dt$ is denoted by Erfc t, being the complement of the error function, so that

$$\text{Erf } t + \text{Erfc } t = \int_0^\infty e^{-t^2} dt = \tfrac{1}{2} \sqrt{\pi}.$$

These functions occur in several branches of Applied Mathematics. A table of values of Erfc t to eight places of decimals was computed by Kramp ("Analyse des Réfractions Astronomiques et Terrestres," Strasbourg, 1799), and from this the existing tables of the Probability Integral have been derived.

which is the probability that an error shall be numerically less than the error x whose ratio to the probable error is z.

54. By means of the tables of the probability integral, comparisons have been made between the actual frequency with which given errors occur in a system containing a large number of observations and their probabilities in accordance with the law of facility.

The following example is given by Bessel in the *Fundamenta Astronomiae.* From 470 observations made by Bradley on the right ascensions of Procyon and Altair, the probable error of a single observation was found (by the formula given in the next section) to be

$$r = 0''.2637 .$$

With this value of r, the probability that an error shall be numerically less than $0''.1$ is found by entering Table II with the argument

$$z = \frac{0''.1}{0''.2637} = 0.3792 ,$$

and the probability that it shall be less than $0''.2$, $0''.3$ and so on, by entering the table with the successive multiples of this quantity. In the annexed table the first column contains the successive values of the limiting error x, the second those of z,

x	z	P	Differences.	Theoretical Nos. of Errors.	Actual Nos. of Errors.
0''.1	0.379	0.2018	0.2018	94.8	94
0 .2	0.758	0.3907	0.1889	88.8	88
0 .3	1.138	0.5573	0.1666	78.3	78
0 .4	1.517	0.6937	0.1364	64.1	58
0 .5	1.896	0.7990	0.1053	49.5	51
0 .6	2.275	0.8751	0.0761	35.8	36
0 .7	2.654	0.9265	0.0514	24.2	26
0 .8	3.034	0.9593	0.0328	15.4	14
0 .9	3.413	0.9787	0.0194	9.1	10
1 .0	3.792	0.9894	0.0107	5.0	7
∞	∞	1.0000	0.0106	5.0	8

and the third the corresponding values of the probability of an error less than x as given by Table II. The fourth column contains the successive differences of these, so that each of the numbers contained in it is the probability of an error falling between the corresponding value of x and that which precedes it. The fifth column contains the multiples of these by 470, which are the theoretical numbers of errors to be expected within the intervals, the last number in the column being the number of errors which should exceed $1''.0$. Finally, the last column contains the actual numbers of errors which occurred in the corresponding intervals, as given by Bessel. The agreement between the theoretical and actual numbers is remarkably close, and forms a practical confirmation of the adopted law of facility.

The Distribution of Errors on a Plane Area.

55. The deviations of the bullet marks in target practice from the point aimed at are of the nature of accidental errors. It is usually assumed that the lateral deviations and the vertical deviations are independent of one another, and that each follows the law of facility for linear errors. We proceed to determine the resulting law of the distribution of the shots upon the plane area.

Let the point aimed at be taken as the origin of coordinates, the horizontal deviation of a shot being denoted by x and the vertical deviations by y, and let these deviations be assumed to have the same measure of precision. Then the probability of a horizontal deviation between x and $x + dx$ is

$$\frac{h}{\sqrt{\pi}} e^{-h^2 x^2} dx;$$

and for each value of x the probability of a vertical deviation between y and $y + dy$ is

$$\frac{h}{\sqrt{\pi}} e^{-h^2 y^2} dy.$$

Hence the probability of hitting the elementary rectangular area $dxdy$, which involves the joint occurrence of these deviations, is

$$\frac{h^2}{\pi} e^{-h^2(x^2+y^2)}dxdy;$$

and, since the probability of hitting an elementary area is proportional to the area, if a denote such an area situated at the point (x, y), the probability of hitting it is

$$\frac{h^2}{\pi} e^{-h^2r^2}a,$$

where r denotes the distance of a from the origin.

Thus the hypothesis of independent vertical and horizontal deviations, each following the usual law of facility and having the same measure of precision, leads to the conclusion that the facility of the resultant deflection depends solely upon its linear amount, r, and not at all upon its direction.* This agrees with

---

* Sir John Herschel's proof of the law of facility of errors (*Edinburgh Review*, July, 1850) rests upon the assumption that it must possess the property which is above shown to belong to the exponential law. He compares accidental errors to the deviations of a stone which is let fall with the intention of hitting a certain mark, and assumes that the deviations in the directions of any two rectangular axes are independent. But, since there is no reason why the resultant deviations should depend upon their direction, this implies that, $f(x^2)$ being the law of facility, we must have

$$f(x^2)f(y^2) = f(x'^2)f(y'^2) = f(x^2 + y^2)f(0)$$

where x' and y' denote coordinates referred to a new set of rectangular axes, so that

$$x^2 + y^2 = x'^2 + y'^2.$$

Now the solution of the functional equation

$$f(x^2)f(v^2) = cf(x^2 + y^2)$$

is

$$f(x^2) = ce^{kx^2}$$

where c and k are constants.

There is no *à priori* reason why the deviations in y should, as assumed

the usual custom of judging of the accuracy of a shot solely by its distance from the point aimed at.

The Surface of Probability.

56. If at every point of the plane of xy we erect a perpendicular z, taking

$$z = \frac{h^2}{\pi} e^{-h^2(x^2 + y^2)},$$

we shall have a *surface of probability* analogous to the curve of probability in the case of linear errors. Since the probability of hitting the elementary area $dx\,dy$ is $z\,dx\,dy$, the probability of hitting any area is the value of the double integral

$$\iint z\,dx\,dy$$

taken over the given area. That is to say, it is the volume of the right cylinder having this area for its base, and having its upper surface in the surface of probability.

The probability surface is a surface of revolution. The solid included between it and the plane of xy is in fact similar to that employed in Art. 39, in evaluating the integral $\displaystyle\int_{-\infty}^{\infty} e^{-h^2 x^2} dx$.

The Probability of Hitting a Rectangle.

57. The probability of hitting the rectangle included between the horizontal lines $y = y_1$, $y = y_2$ and the vertical lines $x = x_1$, $x = x_2$ is the double integral

$$\frac{h^2}{\pi} \int_{x_1}^{x_2} \int_{y_1}^{y_2} e^{-h^2 x^2} e^{-h^2 y^2} dy\,dx,$$

---

above, occur with the same relative frequency when x has one value as when it has another; but it is noteworthy that, having made this assumption, no other law of facility of linear deviation would produce a law of distribution in area involving only the distance from the centre. On the other hand, no other law of distribution in area depending only upon r (such for example as e^{-r}) would make the law of facility for deviations in y independent of the value of x.

which, because the limits for each variable are independent of the other, is equivalent to

$$\frac{h}{\sqrt{\pi}} \int_{x_1}^{x_2} e^{-h^2 x^2} dx \cdot \frac{h}{\sqrt{\pi}} \int_{y_1}^{y_2} e^{-h^2 y^2} dy;$$

that is, it is the product of the probabilities that x and y respectively shall fall between their given limits. This result is, of course, nothing more than the expression of the hypothesis made in Art. 55.[*] If h be known, the values of the factors in the expression (2) may be derived from Table I, as explained in Art. 44.

In particular, putting $x_1 = -\delta$, $x_2 = \delta$, $y_1 = -\delta'$, $y_2 = \delta'$, we have for the probability of hitting a rectangle whose centre is at the origin and whose sides are 2δ and $2\delta'$,

$$p = P_\delta P_{\delta'},$$

where P_δ and $P_{\delta'}$ are tabular results taken from Table I, if h be given, or from Table II if the probable error of the deviations be given.

For example, for the square whose centre is the origin and whose half side is r_1, the probable error of the component deviations, the probability of hitting is $\frac{1}{4}$.

Again, to find the side of the centrally situated square which is as likely as not to be hit, and which therefore may be called *the probable square*, we must determine the value of δ for which $P_\delta = \sqrt{\frac{1}{2}} = 0.7071$. This will be found to correspond to $t = 0.7437$, whence the side of the square is 2δ, where

$$\delta = \frac{t}{h} = \frac{0.7437}{h}.$$

---

[*] The property of the probability surface corresponding to the assumption that the relative frequency of the deviations in y is independent of the value of x is that any section parallel to the plane of yz may be derived from the central section in that plane by reducing all the values of z in the same ratio. In accordance with the preceding foot-note, this is the only surface of revolution possessing this property.

The Probability of Hitting a Circle.

58. Putting $a = 2\pi r dr$ in the expression derived in Art. 55, the probability of hitting the elementary annular area between the circumferences whose radii are r and $r + dr$ is found to be

$$dp = 2h^2 e^{-h^2 r^2} r dr. \qquad \ldots \ldots \quad (1)$$

Hence the probability that the distance of a shot from the point aimed at shall fall between r_1 and r_2 is

$$p = 2h^2 \int_{r_1}^{r_2} e^{-h^2 r^2} r dr = e^{-h^2 r_1^2} - e^{-h^2 r_2^2}. \quad \ldots \quad (2)$$

Putting the lower limit r_1 equal to zero, we have, for the probability of planting a shot within the circle whose radius is r,

$$p = 1 - e^{-h^2 r^2}, \qquad \ldots \ldots \quad (3)$$

a formula in which h is the measure of the accuracy of the marksman.

The Radius of the Probable Circle.

59. If we denote by a the value of r corresponding to $p = \frac{1}{2}$ in equation (3) of the preceding article, we shall have

$$e^{-h^2 a^2} = \tfrac{1}{2}, \qquad \ldots \ldots \ldots \quad (1)$$

whence

$$a = \frac{\sqrt{\log 2}}{h}. \qquad \ldots \ldots \quad (2)$$

Then a is the radius of *the probable circle*, that is, the circle within which a shot is as likely as not to fall, or within which in the long run the marksman can plant half his shots. Thus a is analogous to the probable error in the case of linear deviations, and, being inversely proportional to h, may be taken as an inverse measure of the skill of the marksman.

Eliminating h from the formula for p by means of equation (1), we obtain

$$p = 1 - \left(\frac{1}{2}\right)^{\frac{r^2}{a^2}}. \qquad \ldots \ldots \quad (3)$$

Denoting by n the whole number of shots, and by m the number of those which miss a circular target of radius r, we may, if n and m be sufficiently large, put

$$1 - p = \frac{m}{n}.$$

Supposing p in equation (3) to be thus determined, we derive the formula

$$a = r \sqrt{\frac{\log 2}{\log n - \log m}},$$

in which the ordinary tabular logarithms may be employed.*

The Most Probable Distance.

60. Equation (1), Art. 58, shows that the probability of hitting the elementary annulus of radius r is proportional to

$$re^{-h^2r^2}.$$

The value of r which makes this function a maximum is found to be identical with ε, the mean error of the linear deviations, namely,

$$\varepsilon = \frac{1}{h\sqrt{2}},$$

which is therefore the most probable distance† at which a shot can fall.

This distance might, like a, be taken as the inverse measure of the skill of the marksman.

---

* This is Sir John Herschel's formula for the inverse measure of the skill of the marksman. See " Familiar Lectures on Scientific Subjects," p. 498. London and New York, 1867.

† The point at which the probability is a maximum (that is, where the density of the shots in the long run is the greatest) is of course the origin, at which the ordinate z in the probability surface is a maximum. The value of r here determined is that for which the right cylindrical surface included between the plane of xy and the probability surface is a maximum, that is, the annulus which contains the greatest number of shot in the long run.

Measures of the Accuracy of Shooting.

61. Any quantity inversely proportional to h might be taken as the measure of the marksman's risk of error, or inverse measure of precision. We may employ for this purpose either a, the radius of the probable error, ε, the most probable distance, δ, the half side of the probable square (Art. 57), or r_1, the probable error of a linear deviation.

The most probable value of h derivable from n given shots will be shown in the next section, Art. 73, to be

$$h = \sqrt{\frac{n}{\Sigma r^2}}.$$

Employing this value of h we have

$$a = \frac{\sqrt{\log 2}}{h} = 0.8326 \sqrt{\frac{\Sigma r^2}{n}},$$

$$\varepsilon = \frac{1}{h\sqrt{2}} \quad = 0.7071 \sqrt{\frac{\Sigma r^2}{n}} = \sqrt{\frac{\Sigma r^2}{2n}},$$

$$\delta = \frac{0.7437}{h} \quad = 0.7437 \sqrt{\frac{\Sigma r^2}{n}},$$

$$r_1 = \frac{\rho}{h} \quad = 0.4769 \sqrt{\frac{\Sigma r^2}{n}}.$$

Examples.

1. Show that the abscissa of the point of inflexion in the probability curve is the mean error.

2. In 1000 observations of the same quantity how many may be expected to differ from the mean value by less than the probable error, by less than the mean absolute error, and by less than the mean error respectively?   500, 575, 683.

3. An astronomer measures an angle 100 times; if, when the unit employed is $1''$, the measure of precision is known to be

$h = \frac{1}{5}$, how many errors may be expected to have a numerical value between $2''$ and $4''$? 31.

4. In 125 observations whose probable error is $2''$, how many errors less than $1''$ are to be expected? 33.

5. If the probable error is ten times the least count of the instrument, show that about 27 observations out of 1000 will be recorded with the true value, and 21 will exceed it by an amount equal to the probable error.

6. If h is changed to mh $(m > 1)$, errors less than a certain error x_1 are more probable, and errors greater than x_1 are less probable. Find t_1 the reduced value of x_1.

$$t_1 = hx_1 = \sqrt{\frac{\log m}{m^2 - 1}}.$$

7. Show that the envelop of the probability curve, when h varies, is the hyperbola

$$xy = \frac{1}{\sqrt{(2\pi e)}},$$

the abscissa of the point of contact being the mean error.

8. Show that

$$\int_0^\infty e^{-x^2} dx = x \int_0^\infty e^{-x^2 u^2} du;$$

and thence derive the value of the integral.

9. Deduce the formula of reduction (m positive)

$$\int_0^\infty x^m e^{-h^2 x^2} dx = \frac{m-1}{2h^2} \int_0^\infty x^{m-2} e^{-h^2 x^2} dx;$$

and thence show that (n being a positive integer) the mean value of the $2n$th power of the error is

$$\frac{(2n)!}{2^2 \, n! \, h^n},$$

and that the mean absolute value of the $(2n + 1)$th power of the error is

$$\frac{n!}{h^{2n+1} \sqrt{\pi}}.$$

10. Show that

$$\text{Erf } t = \int_0^t e^{-t^2} dt = t - \frac{t^3}{3} + \frac{1}{2!} \frac{t^5}{5} - \frac{1}{3!} \frac{t^7}{7} + \cdots$$

11. Deduce the formula of reduction (n positive)

$$\int_t^\infty t^{-n} e^{-t^2} dt = \frac{e^{-t^2}}{2t^{n+1}} - \frac{n+1}{2} \int_t^\infty t^{-(n+2)} e^{-t^2} dt;$$

and thence show that

$$\text{Erfc } t = \int_t^\infty e^{-t^2} dt = \frac{e^{-t^2}}{2t} \left(1 - \frac{1}{2t^2} + \frac{1 \cdot 3}{2^2 t^4} - \frac{1 \cdot 3 \cdot 5}{2^3 t^6} + \cdots \right).$$

12. Find the probability that the deviation of a shot shall exceed $2a$. $\frac{1}{16}$.

13. Find the probability that a shot shall fall within the circle whose radius is ε. $1 - e^{-\frac{1}{2}} = 0.3935$.

14. A marksman shoots 500 times at a target; if his skill is such that when errors are measured in feet, $h = 1$, what is the number of bullet marks between two circles described from the centre with radii 1 and 2 feet? 175.

15. If errors are measured in inches in example 14, what are the values of h and of a? $\frac{1}{12}$, 9.99.

16. An archer is observed to plant 9 per cent of his arrows within a circle one foot in diameter; what is the diameter of a target which he might make an even bet to hit at the first shot? 2 ft. 8½ in.

17. A hits a target 3 feet in diameter 51 times out of 79 shots; B hits one 2 feet in diameter 39 times out of 87 shots. Find the diameters of the targets that each can make an even wager to hit at the first shot. For A, 2.45 feet; for B, 2.16 feet.

18. In example 17, what are the odds that B will hit A's probable circle at the first shot? About 59 to 41.

19. If the circular target which a marksman has an even chance of hitting be divided by circumferences cutting the radius into four equal parts, how many shots out of 1000 will fall in the respective areas? 42, 117, 164, 177.

20. A circular target 32 inches in diameter is divided into rings by circumferences cutting the radius into four equal parts. The number of shots out of 1000 which fell in the several areas were 31, 89, 121, 141 ; what are the respective values of a in inches determined from the numbers of shots in the several circles ?   18.764, 18.628, 19.025, 19.202.

21. Find the probability of hitting a square target circumscribing the circle whose radius is a.   .5790.

22. If several shots be fired at a wafer on a wall and the wafer be subsequently removed, show that the centre of gravity of the shot marks is the most probable position of the wafer.

V.

THE COMBINATION OF OBSERVATIONS AND PROBABLE ACCURACY OF THE RESULTS.

The Probability of the Arithmetical Mean.

62. We have seen that, in accordance with the law of facility which we have adopted, the best result of the combination of a number of equally good observations is their arithmetical mean. We have next to determine the probable accuracy of this result, and then to consider the best method of combining observations of unequal precision.

Let there be n observations, the law of facility of error for each of which is

$$y = \frac{h}{\sqrt{\pi}}\, e^{-h^2 (x-a)^2}, \quad \cdots \quad (1)$$

a being the true value of the observed quantity, and $x_1, x_2 \ldots x_n$ the observed values. Then the value of P, equation (2), Art. 36, becomes

$$P = \frac{h^n}{\pi^{\frac{1}{2}n}}\, e^{-h^2 \Sigma (x-a)^2} \Delta x^n; \quad \cdots \quad (2)$$

and, as shown in Art. 30, the probabilities of the different hypotheses which we can make as to the value of a are proportional to the corresponding values of P.

63. Let us now take a to denote the arithmetical mean, and put $a - \delta$ for the true value, so that δ is the error of the arithmetical mean; then denoting the residual by v, the true error will be $x - a + \delta = v + \delta$. It was shown in Art. 43 that

$$\Sigma (v + \delta)^2 = \Sigma v^2 + n\delta^2;$$

hence the general value of P must now be written

$$P = \frac{h^n}{\pi^{\frac{1}{2}n}}\, e^{-h^2 [\Sigma v^2 + n\delta^2]} \Delta x^n, \quad \cdots \quad (3)$$

and the value expressed by equation (2) is now the maximum value, corresponding to $\delta = 0$. Distinguishing this value by the symbol P_0, equation (3) may be written

$$P = P_0 e^{-nh^2\delta^2}. \quad \ldots \quad \ldots \quad (4)$$

Since the probability of δ, which is the error of our final determination, is proportional to P, and P_0 is independent of δ, equation (4) shows that the arithmetical mean has a law of probability which is identical with that which we have adopted in equation (1) for the single observations, except that nh^2 takes the place of h^2. Thus, denoting by y_0 the facility of error in the arithmetical mean, we have

$$y_0 = \frac{h\sqrt{n}}{\sqrt{\pi}} e^{-nh^2\delta^2}. \quad \ldots \quad \ldots \quad (5)$$

The fact that the assumption of the law (1) for a single observation implies a law of the same form for the final value determined from the combined observations is one of the confirmations of this law alluded to in Art. 40.*

64. Equation (5) of the preceding article shows that the arithmetical mean of n observations may be regarded as an observation made with a more precise instrument, the new measure of precision being found by multiplying that of the single observations by $\sqrt{n}$. Since hr is constant when r represents any one of the measures of risk, we have for *the probable error of the arithmetical mean,*

$$r_0 = \frac{r}{\sqrt{n}},$$

---

*In general, an assumed law, $y = \phi(x)$, of facility of error for the single observations would produce a law of a different form for the result determined from n observations. Laplace has shown that whatever be the form of ϕ for the single observations, the law of facility of error in the arithmetical mean approaches indefinitely to

$$y = ce^{-h^2x^2}$$

as a limiting form, when n is increased without limit. See the memoir "On the Law of Facility of Errors of Observation, and on the Method of Least Squares," by J. W. L. Glaisher, *Memoirs Royal Ast. Soc.*, vol. **xxxix.** pp. 104, 105.

and the same relation holds in the case of either of the other measures of risk.

Thus, for example, it is necessary to take four observations in order to double the precision, or reduce the risk of error to one half its original value.

The probable error of a final result is frequently written after it with the sign $\pm$. Thus, if the final determination of an angle is given as $36° \, 42'.3 \pm 1'.22$, the meaning is that the true value of the angle is exactly as likely to lie between the limits thus assigned (that is, between $36° \, 41'.08$ and $36° \, 43'.52$) as it is to lie outside of these limits.

The Combination of Observations of Unequal Precision.

65. When the observations are not equally good, let h_1, h_2, ... h_n be their respective measures of precision; so that, a being the true value, the facility of error of x_1 is

$$y_1 = \frac{h_1}{\sqrt{\pi}} \, e^{-h_1^2 (x_1 - a)^2},$$

that of x_2 is

$$y_2 = \frac{h_2}{\sqrt{\pi}} \, e^{-h_2^2 (x_2 - a)^2},$$

and so on. The value of P, Art. 36, which expresses the probability of the given system of observed values on the hypothesis of a given value of a, now becomes

$$P = \frac{h_1 h_2 \ldots h_n}{\pi^{\frac{1}{2}n}} \, e^{-\Sigma h^2 (x-a)^2} \, \varDelta x_1 \varDelta x_2 \ldots \varDelta x_n; \quad . \quad (1)$$

and, as before, the probabilities of different values of a are proportional to the values they give to P.

It follows that that value of a is most probable which makes $\Sigma h^2 (x - a)^2$ or

$$h_1^2 (x_1 - a)^2 + h_2^2 (x_2 - a)^2 + \ldots + h_n^2 (x_n - a)^2 = \text{a minimum.} \quad (2)$$

In other words, if the error of each observation be multiplied by the corresponding measure of precision, so as to reduce the errors to the same relative value (see Art. 47), *it is necessary that the sum of the squares of the reduced errors should be a minimum.* This is, in fact, the more general statement of the principle of Least Squares.

Differentiating with respect to a, we have

$$h_1^2(x_1 - a) + h_2^2(x_2 - a) + \ldots + h_n^2(x_n - a) = 0; \quad (3)$$

and the value of a determined from this equation is

$$a = \frac{h_1^2 x_1 + h_2^2 x_2 + \ldots + h_n^2 x_n}{h_1^2 + h_2^2 + \ldots + h_n^2} = \frac{\Sigma h^2 x}{\Sigma h^2}, \quad \cdot \quad (4)$$

which is therefore the most probable value of a which can be derived from the n observations.

Weights and Measures of Precision.

66. The value of a found above is in fact the weighted arithmetical mean of the observed values (see Art. 11), when the respective values of h^2 are taken as the weights. But, since the weights are numbers with whose ratios only we are concerned, we may use any proportional numbers $p_1, p_2, \ldots p_n$, in place of the values of h. Thus putting

$$h_1^2 = p_1 h^2, \quad h_2^2 = p_2 h^2, \quad \ldots \quad h_n^2 = p_n h^2, \quad \cdot \quad (5)$$

equation (4) may be written

$$a = \frac{p_1 x_1 + p_2 x_2 + \ldots + p_n x_n}{p_1 + p_2 + \ldots + p_n} = \frac{\Sigma p x}{\Sigma p}. \quad \cdot \quad (6)$$

Hence the most probable value which can be derived from the n observations is *the weighted arithmetical mean, the weights of the observations being proportional to the squares of their measures of precision.*

The quantity h in equations (5) is the measure of precision of an observation whose weight is unity. It is immaterial whether such an observation actually exists among the n observations or not.

If each of the observations has the weight unity, Σp takes the value n, and the value of a becomes the ordinary arithmetical mean.

The Probability of the Weighted Mean.

67. Let us now, employing a to denote the value determined above, put $a + \delta$ in place of a in the value of P, so that δ represents the error in our final determination of a. Then, writing v for the residual, we have, as in Art. 63, to replace $x - a$ by $v + \delta$. The value of P, equation (1), Art. 65, thus becomes

$$P = \frac{h_1 h_2 \ldots h_n}{\pi^{\frac{1}{2}n}} e^{-\Sigma h^2 (v+\delta)^2} \Delta x_1 \Delta x_2 \ldots \Delta x_n$$

Now, by equation (3), $\Sigma h^2 v = 0$, therefore

$$\Sigma h^2 (v + \delta)^2 = \Sigma h^2 v^2 + \delta^2 \Sigma h^2 \cdot$$

substituting, we obtain

$$P = \frac{h_1 h_2 \ldots h_n}{\pi^{\frac{1}{2}n}} e^{-\Sigma h^2 v^2} e^{-\delta^2 \Sigma h^2} \Delta x_1 \Delta x_2 \ldots \Delta x_n.$$

Hence, putting P_0 for the value assumed by P when $\delta = 0$, we have

$$P = P_0 e^{-\delta^2 (h_1^2 + h_2^2 + \ldots + h_n^2)}.$$

Since the probability of δ is proportional to P, it follows, as in Art. 63, that the law of facility of the mean is of the same form as those of the separate observations, the square of the new measure of precision being the sum of the squares of those of the separate observations. Denoting the facility of error in the weighted mean by y_0, and employing the notation of Art. 66, we have therefore

$$y_0 = \frac{h \sqrt{\Sigma p}}{\sqrt{\pi}} e^{-\delta^2 h^2 \Sigma p},$$

in which h is the measure of precision of an observation whose weight is unity. When the weights are all equal, this formula becomes identical with that of Art. 63.

68. The weight of the mean is defined in Art. 12 to be Σp, the sum of the weights of the constituent observations. Hence the value of y_0 found above shows that, *in comparing the final result with any single observation*, as well as in comparing the observations with one another, *the measures of precision are proportional to the square roots of the weights*.

The probable error being inversely proportional to h, it follows that, r representing the probable error of an observation whose weight is unity, and r_0 that of the mean whose weight is Σp, we shall have

$$r_0 = \frac{r}{\sqrt{\Sigma p}}.$$

This result includes that of Art. 64, and, like it, is applicable to either of the measures of risk.

The Most Probable Value of h derivable from a System of Observations.

69. Substituting the values of $h_1, h_2, \ldots h_n$ in terms of the weights, equations (5), Art. 66, the value of P, equation (1), Art. 65, becomes

$$P = \frac{\sqrt{(p_1 p_2 \ldots p_n)}}{\pi^{\frac{1}{2}n}} \, h^n e^{-h^2 \Sigma p \, (x-a)^2} \varDelta x_1 \varDelta x_2 \ldots \varDelta x_n. \quad (1)$$

The same principle which we have employed to determine the most probable value of the observed quantity serves to determine the most probable value of h. Thus the most probable value of h is that which gives the greatest value to P, or, omitting factors independent of h, to the expression

$$h^n e^{-h^2 \Sigma p \, (x-a)^2}.$$

Putting the derivative of this expression equal to zero, we have

$$e^{-h^2 \Sigma p (x-a)^2} \left[n h^{n-1} - 2 h^{n+1} \Sigma p \, (x-a)^2 \right] = 0;$$

whence

$$h = \sqrt{\frac{n}{2\Sigma p(x-a)^2}}, \quad \cdots \quad (2)$$

in which a denotes the true value of the observed quantity.

70. Equation (2) may be written

$$\frac{\Sigma p(x-a)^2}{n} = \frac{1}{2h^2} \cdots \cdots (1)$$

When the observations are all made under the same circumstances, so that we may put

$$p_1 = p_2 = \ldots = p_n = 1,$$

the equation becomes

$$\frac{\Sigma(x-a)^2}{n} = \frac{1}{2h^2}, \quad \cdots \cdots (2)$$

in which h denotes the measure of precision of each of the observations. The second member of this equation is the value of ε^2, the square of the " mean error," which was defined in Art. 50 as the mean value of the square of the error, having regard to its probability in a system of observations whose measure of precision is h. In other words, it is the mean squared error in an unlimited number of observations made under the given circumstances of observation.

On the other hand, the first member of equation (2) is the actual mean squared error for the n given observations. The square root of this quantity may be called the *observational* value of the mean error, in distinction from the *theoretical* value, ε, which is a fixed function of h.

Thus the equation asserts that the most probable value of h is found *by assuming the theoretical value of the mean error to be the same as its observational value.* In other words, it is a consequence of the accepted law of facility that the measure of precision of a set of observations equally good is proportional to the reciprocal of the mean error as determined from the observations themselves.

Formulæ for the Mean and Probable Errors.

71. The quantity $\Sigma p(x - a)^2$ in the value of h, equation (2), Art. 69, is the sum of the weighted squares of the actual errors of the observed values $x_1, x_2, \ldots x_n$. Now, when a denotes the weighted arithmetical mean, $x - a$ must be replaced by $v + \delta$, as in Art. 67, and

$$\Sigma p(v + \delta)^2 = \Sigma p v^2 + \delta^2 \Sigma p. \quad \ldots \quad (1)$$

The value of δ, which is the error of the arithmetical mean, is of course unknown; it may be either positive or negative, but, since δ^2 is essentially positive, the true value of $\Sigma p(x - a)^2$ always exceeds $\Sigma p v^2$. The best correction we can apply to the approximate value $\Sigma p v^2$ is found by giving to δ^2 in equation (1) its mean value; for, by adopting this as a general rule we shall commit the least error in the long run. Now we have seen in Art. 67 that δ follows a law of probability of the usual form in which the measure of precision is $h\sqrt{\Sigma p}$, hence the mean value of δ^2 is the same as the mean squared error found in Art. 50, except that h is changed to $h\sqrt{\Sigma p}$. That is to say, the mean value of δ^2 is

$$\frac{1}{2h^2 \Sigma p}.$$

Putting this in place of δ^2 in equation (1) we have

$$\Sigma p(v + \delta)^2 = \Sigma p v^2 + \frac{1}{2h^2}. \quad \ldots \quad (2)$$

Equation (2), Art. 69, may be written in the form

$$\frac{n}{h^2} = 2\Sigma p(x - a)^2,$$

and, employing the value just determined, we have

$$\frac{n}{h^2} = 2\Sigma p v^2 + \frac{1}{h^2};$$

whence we derive

$$h = \sqrt{\frac{n - 1}{2\Sigma p v^2}} \quad \ldots \quad (3)$$

for the most probable value of h for an observation of weight unity.

72. The resulting value of the mean error of an observation whose weight is unity is

$$\varepsilon = \frac{1}{h\sqrt{2}} = \sqrt{\frac{\Sigma p v^2}{n-1}}, \quad \cdots \cdots (1)$$

and by Art. 68, the mean error of the arithmetical mean whose weight is Σp is

$$\varepsilon_0 = \sqrt{\frac{\Sigma p v^2}{(n-1)\Sigma p}}. \quad \cdots \cdots (2)$$

Again, the value of the probable error of an observation whose weight is unity is

Probable error of an observation

$$r = \frac{\rho}{h} = \rho\sqrt{2}\sqrt{\frac{\Sigma p v^2}{n-1}} = 0.6745\sqrt{\frac{\Sigma p v^2}{n-1}}, \quad \cdot (3)$$

and that of the weighted arithmetical mean is

Probable error of Arithmetical mean

$$r_0 = 0.6745\sqrt{\frac{\Sigma p v^2}{(n-1)\Sigma p}}. \quad \cdots \cdots (4)$$

The constant 0.6745 is the reciprocal of that which occurs in equation (2), Art. 51.

For a set of equally good observations we have, by putting $p_1 = p_2 = \ldots = p_n = 1$,

$$r = 0.6745\sqrt{\frac{\Sigma v^2}{n-1}} \quad \cdots \cdots (5)$$

for the probable error of a single observation, and

$$r_0 = 0.6745\sqrt{\frac{\Sigma v^2}{n(n-1)}} \quad \cdots \cdots (6)$$

for the probable error of the simple arithmetical mean.

The Most Probable Value of h in Target Practice.

73. We have seen in Art. 55 that in target practice the probability of hitting an elementary area a, situated at the distance r from the point aimed at, is

$$\frac{h^2}{\pi} e^{-h^2 r^2} a.$$

Suppose that n shots have been made, the first falling upon the area a_1, the second upon a_2, and so on; then, before the shots were made, the probability that the shots should fall upon these areas in the given succession is

$$P = \frac{h^{2n}}{\pi^n} e^{-h^2 \Sigma r^2} a_1 a_2 \ldots a_n.$$

Hence, the shots having been made, the probabilities of different values of h are proportional to the values they give to the expression

$$h^{2n} e^{-h^2 \Sigma r^2}.$$

Making this function of h a maximum, we have

$$e^{-h^2 \Sigma r^2} [2n h^{2n-1} - 2h^{n+1} \Sigma r^2] = 0,$$

whence we have, for the most probable value of h,

$$h = \sqrt{\frac{n}{\Sigma r^2}},$$

the value quoted in Art. 61.

74. The value of ε^2 hence derived is

$$\varepsilon^2 = \frac{\Sigma r^2}{2n} = \frac{\Sigma x^2 + \Sigma y^2}{2n},$$

where ε is the mean error for the component deviations, which are the values of x and y respectively. The values of ε^2 as determined from the lateral and vertical deviations respectively, are

$$\varepsilon^2 = \frac{\Sigma x^2}{n}, \quad \varepsilon^2 = \frac{\Sigma y^2}{n}.$$

Thus the value of ε^2, which we have derived from the total deviations, or values of r, is the mean of its most probable values as separately derived from the two classes of component deviations.

It will be noticed that neither of the quantities Σx^2, Σy^2 or Σr^2 needs to be corrected as in Art. 71, because we are here dealing with actual errors and not with residuals.*

The Computation of the Probable Error.

75. The annexed table gives an example of the application of formulæ (5) and (6), Art. 72. The seventeen values of x in

x	v	v^2
4.524	+ .0185	.00034225
4.500	− .0055	3025
4.515	+ .0095	9025
4.508	+ .0025	625
4.513	+ .0075	5625
4.511	+ .0055	3025
4.497	− .0085	7225
4.507	+ .0015	225
4.501	− .0045	2025
4.502	− .0035	1225
4.485	− .0205	42025
4.519	+ .0135	18225
4.517	+ .0115	13225
4.504	− .0015	225
4.493	− .0125	15625
4.492	− .0135	18225
4.505	− .0005	25

$$a = 4.505\tfrac{8}{17} = 4.5055 \qquad \Sigma v^2 = .00173825$$

---

*If the position of the point aimed at had been inferred from the shot marks, as in example 22 of the preceding section, it would have been necessary to change n into $n - 1$, as in the case of errors of observation. So also this change should be made when the errors employed are measured from the mean point of impact, as in testing pieces of ordnance.

the first column are independent measurements of the same quantity made by Prof. Rowland for the purpose of determining a certain wave length.   At the foot of the column is the arithmetical mean of the seventeen observations.   The second column contains the residuals found by subtracting this from the separate observations.   The values of v^2 in the third column are taken from a table of squares, and their sum is written at the foot of the column.   Dividing this by 16, the value of $n - 1$, we find

$$\frac{\Sigma v^2}{n - 1} = 0.00010864,$$

and taking the square root,

$$\varepsilon = 0.01042.$$

Multiplying by the constant 0.6745 we have

$$r = 0.00703$$

for the probable error of a single observation.

Again, dividing by $\sqrt{17}$, we have

$$r_0 = 0.00171$$

for the probable error of the final determination, which may therefore be written

$$x = 4.5055 \pm 0.0017.$$

It will be noticed that nine of the residuals are numerically less and eight are numerically greater than the value we have found for the probable error of a single observation.

76. The equation

$$\Sigma(v + \delta)^2 = \Sigma v^2 + n\delta^2,$$

derived in Art. 43, enables us to abridge somewhat the computation of Σv^2, and to reduce the extent to which a table of squares is needed.   Thus, if we use the value of a to three places of decimals, namely $a = 4.505$, in forming the values of

v, each of these quantities will be algebraically greater than it should be by $\frac{8}{17}$ of a unit in the third decimal place. Putting

$$\delta = \tfrac{8}{17}, \quad n\delta^2 = \tfrac{64}{17} = 3\tfrac{13}{17};$$

hence Σv^2, as found on this supposition, will be too great by $3\tfrac{13}{17}$ of a unit in the sixth decimal place. The columns headed v and v^2 would then stand as follows:

v	v^2
+ .019	.000361
− .005	25
+ .010	100
+ .003	9
+ .008	64
+ .006	36
− .008	64
+ .002	4
− .004	16
− .003	9
− .020	400
+ .014	196
+ .012	144
− .001	1
− .012	144
− .013	169
.000	0

$$\Sigma(v + \delta)^2 = .001742$$

and making the correction found above, we have

$$\Sigma v^2 = .001738\tfrac{4}{17},$$

which is the exact value.

The smallness of the correction is due to the fact that Σv^2 is a minimum value. The correction might have been neglected, being, in this case, only about $\frac{1}{30}$ of the correction made in the formula on account of the mean value of the unknown error in the arithmetical mean.

77. As an example of the application of the formulæ involving weights, let us suppose that instead of the seventeen observations in the preceding article we were given only the means of certain groups into which the seventeen observations may be separated. These means we have seen may be regarded as observations having weights equal to the respective numbers of observations from which they are derived. The annexed table presents the

p	x	v	v^2	
2	4.512	+ .0065	.00004225	.00008450
1	4.515	+ .0095	9025	9025
4	4.507	+ .0015	225	900
3	4.503	− .0025	625	1875
2	4.502	− .0035	1225	2450
2	4.511	+ .0055	3025	6050
3	4.497	− .0085	7225	21675

$$a = 4.5055 \qquad \Sigma pv^2 = .00050425$$

data in such a form, the first value of x being the mean of the first two values in the preceding table, the next being the third observation, the next the mean of the following four, and so on. The weighted mean of the present seven values of x of course agrees with the final value before found. The values of v and of v^2 are formed as before, and the values of pv^2 are given in the last column, at the foot of which is the value of Σpv^2. Dividing this by 6, the present value of $n − 1$, we find

$$\frac{\Sigma pv^2}{n - 1} = 0.00008304,$$

and, multiplying the square root of this by 0.6745, the value of the probable error of an observation whose weight is unity is

$$r = 0.00615.$$

The probable error of the weighted mean found by dividing this by $\sqrt{17}$, the value of $\sqrt{\Sigma p}$, is

$$r_0 = 0.00149.$$

78. The value of r found above corresponds to a single observation of the set given in Art. 75. It differs considerably from the value found in that article. The discrepancy is due to the fact that in Art. 76 we did not use all the data given in Art. 75, and it is not to be expected that the most probable value of h which can be deduced from the imperfect data should agree with that deduced from the more complete data. In one case we have seventeen discrepancies from the arithmetical mean, due to accidental errors, upon which to base an estimate of the precision of the observations; in the other case we have but seven discrepancies. The result in the former case is of course more trustworthy; and in general, the larger the value of n, the more confidence can we place in our estimate of the measures of precision.

79. It should be noticed particularly that the weighted observations in Art. 76 are not equivalent to a set of seventeen observations of which two are equal to the first value of x, one to the second, four to the third, and so on, *except in the sense of giving the same mean value.* Compare Art. 10. Such a set would exhibit discrepancies very much smaller on the whole than those of the seventeen observations in Art. 75. Accordingly, the value of ε^2 in the supposed case would be very much smaller than that found above for the weighted observations. The value of Σv^2 would in fact be the same as that of $\Sigma p v^2$ in Art. 76, but it would be divided by 16 instead of by 6.

The approximate equality of the results in Art. 75 and Art. 76 is due to the fact that the v^2's, of which seventeen exist in each sum, are on the average very much diminished* when the mean of a group is substituted for the separate observations, and this

---

* The amount of this diminution is, however, largely a matter of chance. For example, if we had taken the seven groups in such a manner that the successive values of p were 2, 3, 2, 4, 2, 1, 3, we should have found

$$r = 0.00833,$$

differing in excess from that of Art. 75 still more than that obtained above does in defect.

makes up for the change in the denominator by the decrease in the value of n.

80. Different weights are frequently assigned to observations made under different circumstances, according to the judgment of the observer. Thus an astronomer may regard an observation made when the atmosphere is exceptionally clear as worth two of those made under ordinary circumstances. Regarding the latter as standard observations having the weight unity, he will then assign the weight 2 to the former. As explained in the preceding article this is not equivalent to recording two standard observations, each giving the observed value. The latter procedure would lead to an erroneous estimate of the degree of accuracy attained.

The Values of h and r derived from the Mean Absolute Error.

81. The mean absolute error η is a fixed function of h, viz:

$$\eta = \frac{1}{h\sqrt{\pi}}; \quad \cdots \cdots \quad (1)$$

hence, if we were able to determine it independently, we should have a means of finding the value of h, and consequently that of r.

In the case of n equally good observations, let $[x - a]$ denote the numerical value of an error taken as positive, then

$$\frac{\Sigma[x - a]}{n} \quad \cdots \cdots \quad (2)$$

is the arithmetical mean of the absolute values of the n actual errors. This may be called the *observational value* of the mean absolute error in distinction from the *theoretic value* given in equation (1), which is the value of this mean in accordance with the law of probability, when the measure of precision is h.

If we assume these values to be equal, we obtain

$$\frac{\Sigma[x - a]}{n} = \frac{1}{h\sqrt{\pi}},$$

whence

$$h = \frac{n}{\Sigma[x-a]\sqrt{\pi}}, \quad \cdots \quad (3)$$

and

$$r = \frac{\rho}{h} = \rho\sqrt{\pi}\frac{\Sigma[x-a]}{n}. \quad \cdots \quad (4)$$

If in this formula we put for a the arithmetical mean, so that $\Sigma[x-a]$ becomes $\Sigma[v]$, it gives the *apparent probable error*, that is, the value r would have if the arithmetical mean were known to be the true value of x. Denoting this by r', we have then

$$r' = \rho\sqrt{\pi}\frac{\Sigma[v]}{n} = 0.8453\frac{\Sigma[v]}{n}. \quad \cdots \quad (5)$$

82. It is obvious from Arts. 71 and 72 that the values of r' and r as derived from the square of the residuals are

$$r' = 0.6745\sqrt{\frac{\Sigma v^2}{n}}, \qquad r = 0.6745\sqrt{\frac{\Sigma v^2}{n-1}},$$

so that

$$r : r' = \sqrt{n} : \sqrt{(n-1)}.* \quad \cdots \quad (6)$$

---

* This relation between the apparent and the real probable error is derived directly by C. A. F. Peters (*Berliner Astronomisches Nachrichten*, 1856, vol. xliv. p. 29) as follows: If $e_1, e_2, \ldots e_n$ are the true errors, that of the arithmetical mean is

$$\delta = \frac{1}{n}(e_1 + e_2 + \ldots + e_n),$$

then

$$v_1 = e_1 - \delta = \frac{n-1}{n}e_1 - \frac{1}{n}e_2 - \ldots - \frac{1}{n}e_n, \quad \text{etc.}$$

Since r is the probable error of each e, and r' that of each v, the formula for the probable error of a linear function of independent quantities (see Art. 89) gives

$$r'^2 = \left[\left(\frac{n-1}{n}\right)^2 + (n-1)\frac{1}{n^2}\right]r^2 = \frac{n-1}{n}r^2.$$

This result is used by Peters to establish the formula derived above, but it may also be used in place of the method of Art. 71 for the correction of the apparent value of r in terms of Σv^2.

Combining this result with equation (5) we have

$$r = 0.8453 \frac{\Sigma[v]}{\sqrt{[n(n-1)]}}, \quad \cdots \quad (7)$$

and hence, for the probable error of the arithmetical mean,

$$r_0 = 0.8453 \frac{\Sigma[v]}{n\sqrt{(n-1)}}. \quad \cdots \quad (8)$$

As an illustration, let us apply these formulæ to the observations given in Art. 75, for which we find $\Sigma[v] = 0.1405$. Substituting this value, and putting $n = 17$, we find

$$r = 0.00720, \qquad r_0 = 0.00175.$$

These values agree closely with those derived in Art. 75 from the formulæ involving Σv^2, which indeed give the most probable values of r and r_0, but involve much more numerical work, especially when n is large.

83. In order to adapt the formulæ of Art. 82 to the case of weighted observations, it is necessary to reduce the errors to the same scale; in other words, to make them proportional to the reduced errors or values of t, see Art. 47. Since the measures of precision are proportional to the square roots of the weights, this is effected by multiplying each error by the square root of the corresponding weight. The products may be regarded as errors belonging to the same system, namely, that which corresponds to the weight unity.

Hence equation (7) gives for the probable error of an observation whose weight is unity

$$r = 0.8453 \frac{\Sigma[v\sqrt{p}]}{\sqrt{[n(n-1)]}},$$

and for the probable error of the weighted arithmetical mean we have

$$r_0 = 0.8453 \frac{\Sigma[v\sqrt{p}]}{\sqrt{[n(n-1)\Sigma p]}}.$$

Examples.

1. A line is measured five times and the probable error of the mean is .016 of a foot. How many additional measurements of the same precision are required in order to reduce the probable error of the determination to .004 of a foot?   75.

2. It is required to determine an angle with a probable error less than $0''.25$. The mean of twenty measurements gives a probable error of $0''.38$; how many additional measurements are necessary?   27.

3. If the probable error of each of two like measurements of a foot bar is .00477 of an inch, what is the probable error of their mean?   .00337.

4. Ten measurements of the density of a body made with equal precision gave the following results:

9.662,	9.664,	9.677,	9.663,	9.645,
9.673,	9.659,	9.662,	9.680,	9.654.

What is the probable value of the density of the body and the probable error of that value? $9.6639 \pm .0022.$

5. Forty micrometric measurements of the error of position of a division line upon a standard scale gave the following results:

3.68	5.08	2.81	4.43	5.48	4.21	3.28	5.21
3.11	2.95	4.65	3.43	3.76	5.23	3.78	4.43
4.76	6.35	3.27	3.26	4.59	4.45	3.22	2.28
2.75	3.78	4.08	2.48	2.64	3.95	3.98	4.10
4.15	4.49	4.51	4.84	2.98	2.66	3.91	4.18

Find the probable value of the quantity measured and its probable error. $3.930 \pm 0.097.$

6. In the preceding example what is the probable error of a single observed quantity: $1°$, by the formula involving the squares of the errors; $2°$, by that involving the absolute errors? $1°, r = 0.616; 2°, r = 0.618.$

7. An angle in the primary triangulation of the U. S. Coast Survey was measured twenty-four times with the following results:

116° 43′ 44″.45	49.20	51.05	51.75	51.05	49.25
50 .55	48.85	47.85	49.00	51.70	46.75
50 .95	47.40	50.60	52.35	49.05	49.25
48 .90	47.75	48.45	51.30	50.55	53.40

Find the probable error of a single measurement, and the final determination of the angle.   1″.35 : 116° 43′ 49″.64 ± 0″.28.

8. In example 7, taking the means of the six groups of four observations each, determine the probable error of the first of these means: 1°, considered as a measurement of four times the weight of those in example 7; 2°, directly as one of six observations of equal weight; 3°, as a determination from its four constituents.   1°, 0″.67 ; 2°, 0″.72 ; 3°, 1″.00.

9. An interval of 600 units as determined by a micrometer was forty times measured to determine the error in the pitch of the screw, with the following results:

600.0	604.8	600.7	601.4	602.0	602.6	600.0	602.4
599.7	606.1	602.4	603.4	602.7	602.7	600.7	602.4
599.5	604.7	601.6	603.1	603.7	600.9	601.4	602.1
604.6	602.1	601.7	601.8	602.1	601.4	602.9	603.6
603.9	602.2	601.4	600.6	602.3	600.8	602.9	603.6

Find the probable value of the interval and its probable error.   602.22 ± 0.157.

VI.

THE FACILITY OF ERROR IN A FUNCTION OF ONE OR MORE OBSERVED QUANTITIES.

The Linear Function of a Single Observed Quantity.

84. If the value of an observed quantity X be subject to an error x, the value of a given function of X, say $Z = f(X)$, will be subject to a corresponding error z. Assuming x to follow the usual law of facility, h being the measure of precision and r the probable error, we have now to determine the law of facility of z, for any form of the function f.

Let us first consider the linear function

$$Z = mX + b,$$

where m and b are constants. The case is obviously the same as that of the simple multiple mX, the relation between the corresponding errors being

$$z = mx.$$

The probability that the error z falls between z and $z + dz$ is the same as the probability that x falls between x and $x + dx$, namely,

$$\frac{h}{\sqrt{\pi}} e^{-h^2 x^2} dx.$$

Expressing this in terms of z, it becomes

$$\frac{h}{\sqrt{\pi}} e^{-\frac{h^2 z^2}{m^2}} \frac{dz}{m},$$

or, putting $\frac{h}{m} = H$,

$$\frac{H}{\sqrt{\pi}} e^{-H^2 z^2} dz.$$

Thus the law of facility for Z is of the same form as that for X, the measure of precision being found by dividing that of X by m; and, denoting the probable error of Z by R, we have (since probable errors are inversely as the measures of precision)

$$R = mr,$$

and the same relation holds between either of the other measures of the risk of error.

The curves of facility for X and Z are related in the same manner as those drawn in Fig. 4, page 30, and the process of passing from one to the other is that described in Art. 46; that is to say, the abscissas which represent the errors are multiplied by m, and then the ordinates are divided by m, so that the areas standing upon the corresponding bases dx and dz shall remain equal.

Non-Linear Functions of a Single Observed Quantity.

85. A non-linear function of an observed quantity subject to the usual law of facility does not strictly follow a law of facility of the same form. If, however, as is usually the case, the error x is very small, any function of the observed quantity will very nearly follow a law of the usual form. Let a be the true value of the observed quantity, then

$$X = a + x,$$

and

$$Z = f(X) = f(a + x).$$

Expanding by Taylor's Theorem, and neglecting the higher powers of x,[*] we may take

$$Z = f(a) + xf'(a),$$

which is of the linear form. Hence we may regard Z as subject to the usual law of facility, its probable error being

$$R = rf'(a),$$

or, putting the observed value in place of a,

$$R = rf'(X).$$

---

[*] The ratio of the square of the error to the error itself is the value of the error considered as a number, and it is this numerical value which must be small.

The Facility of Error in the Sum or Difference of Two Observed Quantities.

86. Let X and Y be two observed quantities subject to the usual law of facility of error, their measures of precision being h and k respectively.   If

$$Z = X + Y,$$

the relation between the errors of Z, X and Y is obviously

$$z = x + y.$$

In order to find the facility of z, that is, the probability that z shall fall between z and $z + dz$, let us first suppose that x has a definite fixed value.   With this hypothesis, the probability in question is the same as the probability that y shall fall between y and $y + dy$, where

$$y = z - x, \quad \text{and} \quad dy = dz.$$

This probability is

$$\frac{k}{\sqrt{\pi}}\, e^{-k^2 y^2} dy, \quad \text{or} \quad \frac{k}{\sqrt{\pi}}\, e^{-k^2(z-x)^2} dz.$$

Multiplying by the elementary probability of the hypothesis made, which is

$$\frac{h}{\sqrt{\pi}}\, e^{-h^2 x^2} dx,$$

we have

$$\frac{hk}{\pi}\, e^{-h^2 x^2 - k^2(z-x)^2}\, dz\, dx \quad \cdots \cdots \quad (\text{1})$$

for the probability that the required event (namely, the occurrence of the particular value of z) shall happen in this particular way, that is, in connexion with the particular value of x.   To find the total probability of the event we therefore sum the above expression for all possible values of x, thus obtaining

$$\frac{hk}{\pi} \int_{-\infty}^{\infty} e^{-(h^2 + k^2)x^2 + 2k^2 zx - k^2 z^2}\, dz\, dx. \quad \cdots \quad (2)$$

The exponent of e in this expression may be written

$$-(h^2 + k^2)\left(x - \frac{k^2 z}{h^2 + k^2}\right) + \frac{k^4 z^2}{h^2 + k^2} - k^2 z^2;$$

whence, putting $a = \dfrac{k^2 z}{h^2 + k^2}$ and

$$H^2 = k^2 - \frac{k^4}{h^2 + k^2} = \frac{h^2 k^2}{h^2 + k^2}, \quad \cdots \quad (3)$$

the expression (2) becomes

$$\frac{hk dz}{\pi} e^{-H^2 z^2} \int_{-\infty}^{\infty} e^{-(h^2 + k^2)(x - a)^2} dx.$$

Since a is independent of x, the value of the integral contained in this expression is, by Art. 39, $\dfrac{\sqrt{\pi}}{\sqrt{(h^2 + k^2)}}$; hence the probability that z shall fall between z and $z + dz$ is

$$\frac{hk}{\sqrt{\pi}\sqrt{(h^2 + k^2)}} e^{-H^2 z^2} dz, \quad \text{or} \quad \frac{H}{\sqrt{\pi}} e^{-H^2 z^2} dz.$$

87. The result just obtained shows that the sum of two quantities subject to the usual law of facility of error is subject to a law of the same form, its measure of precision being determined by equation (3).

Writing equation (3) in the form

$$\frac{1}{H^2} = \frac{1}{h^2} + \frac{1}{k^2},$$

it is evident that, if r_1, r_2 and R be the probable errors of X, Y and $X + Y$, we shall have

$$R^2 = r_1^2 + r_2^2,$$

the same relation holding in the case of either of the other measures of risk of error.

For the difference

$$Z = X - Y,$$

we have the same result; for the errors of $-Y$ have obviously the same law of facility as those of Y.

88. As an illustration, suppose the latitude φ and the polar distance p of a circumpolar star to be determined from the altitudes of the star at its upper and lower culminations. Since

$$h_1 = \varphi + p \quad \text{and} \quad h_2 = \varphi - p,$$

we have

$$\varphi = \tfrac{1}{2}(h_1 + h_2), \qquad p = \tfrac{1}{2}(h_1 - h_2).$$

Then, r_1 and r_2 denoting the probable errors of h_1 and h_2 respectively, that of $h_1 + h_2$ and also that of $h_1 - h_2$ is $\sqrt{(r_1^2 + r_2^2)}$, hence the probable error both of φ and of p when thus determined is

$$R = \tfrac{1}{2}\sqrt{(r_1^2 + r_2^2)}.$$

The Linear Function of Several Observed Quantities.

89. It follows from Arts. 84 and 87 that the linear function

$$Z = b + m_1 X_1 + m_2 X_2 + \ldots + m_n X_n \quad . \quad . \quad . \quad (1)$$

of n observed quantities is subject to the usual law of facility,* its probable error being

$$R = \sqrt{(m_1^2 r_1^2 + m_2^2 r_2^2 + \ldots + m_n^2 r_n^2)}, \quad . \quad . \quad (2)$$

where $r_1, r_2, \ldots r_n$ are the probable errors of the several observed quantities.

In particular, if the n quantities have the same probable error r, the probable error of their sum is $r\sqrt{n}$. The probable error of their arithmetical mean, which is $\dfrac{1}{n}$ of this sum, is therefore $\dfrac{r}{\sqrt{n}}$. This result agrees with that found in Art. 64, where,

---

* The fact that the law of facility thus reproduces itself has often been regarded as confirmatory of its truth. This property of the law $ce^{-h^2 x^2}$ results from its being a limiting form for the facility of error in the linear function Z, when n is large, whatever be the forms of the facility functions for $X_1, X_2, \ldots X_n$. Compare the foot-note on page 49, and see the memoir there referred to. It follows that " we shall obtain the same law $e^{-h^2 x^2}$ (for a single observed quantity) if we regard each actual error as formed by the linear combination of a large number of errors due to different independent sources."

however, the n quantities were all observed values of the same quantity, and the arithmetical mean was under consideration by virtue of its being the most probable value in accordance with the law of facility.

90. It is to be noticed that in formula (2) it is essential that the probable errors r_1, r_2, ... r_n should be the results of independent determinations. For example, in the illustration given in Art. 88, we have $h_1 = \varphi + p$, whence we should expect to find

$$(\text{prob. err. of } h_1)^2 = (\text{prob. err. of } \varphi)^2 + (\text{prob. err. of } p)^2 ;$$

but it will be found that this is not true when the probable errors of φ and of p are determined as in that article. In fact, in the demonstration given in Art. 86, it is assumed that the law of facility for Y holds true when X has a definite fixed value; but in the present illustration the law of facility found for φ does not hold true for a definite fixed value of p.*

The Non-Linear Function of Several Observed Quantities.

91. Supposing, as in Art. 85, that the errors of the observed quantities are small compared to the quantities themselves, we may replace any function by an approximately equivalent function of a linear form. Thus, denoting the true values of the observed quantities X_1, X_2, ... X_n by a_1, a_2, ... a_n, we have

$$Z = f(X_1, X_2, \ldots X_n) = f(a_1 + x_1, a_2 + x_2, \ldots a_n + x_n).$$

Expanding, and neglecting powers and products of the small quantities x_1, x_2, ... x_n, we obtain the approximate value

$$Z = f(a_1, a_2, \ldots a_n) + x_1 \frac{df}{da_1} + x_2 \frac{df}{da_2} + \ldots + x_n \frac{df}{da_n},$$

which is of the linear form. Hence, in accordance with equation (2), Art. 89, the probable error of Z may be determined by the equation

$$R^2 = r_1^2 \left(\frac{df}{dX_1}\right)^2 + r_2^2 \left(\frac{df}{dX_2}\right)^2 + \ldots + r_n^2 \left(\frac{df}{dX_n}\right)^2.$$

---

* If the value of p were known, each value of h_1 would imply a special value of h_2, and therefore the probability of ϕ would no longer be that found in Art. 88.

Examples.

1. If the probable error in measuring the radius a of a circle is r, what are the probable errors of the circumference and of the area? $2\pi r; \; 2\pi ar.$

2. What is the probable error of $\log_{10} x$, r being the probable error of x? $0.4343 \dfrac{r}{x}.$

3. If measurements of adjacent sides of a rectangle give $a \pm r_1$ and $b \pm r_2$, what is the probable error of the area ab?

$$\sqrt{(b^2 r_1^2 + a^2 r_2^2)}.$$

4. If the rectangle is found to be a square and the sides are measured with the same precision, show that the probable error of the area is the same as if it were known to be a square; but if r_1 and r_2 are not equal, the area is obtained with less accuracy than it would be if it were known to be a square.

5. An angle observation is the difference between two readings of the limb of the instrument; if r is the probable error of the angle, what is the probable error of each reading? $\dfrac{r}{\sqrt{2}}.$

6. The zenith distance of a star observed in the meridian is

$$\zeta = 21° \; 17' \; 20''.3, \text{ with the mean error } 2''.3,$$

and the declination of the star is given

$$\delta = 19° \; 30' \; 14''.8, \text{ with the mean error } 0''.8:$$

what is the mean error of the latitude of the place of observation found from the formula $\varphi = \zeta + \delta$?

$$\varphi = 40° \; 47' \; 35''.1, \text{ with the mean error } 2''.44.$$

7. The latitude of a place has been found with the mean error $0''.25$, and the meridian zenith distance of stars observed at that place with a certain instrument has been found to be subject to the mean error $0''.62$; what is the mean error of the declinations of the stars deduced by the formula $\delta = \varphi - \zeta$? $0''.67.$

8. The correction of a chronometer is found to be $+ 12^m \; 13^s.2$, with the mean error $0^s.3$; ten days later the correction is found to be $+ 12^m \; 21^s.4$, with the same mean error; what is the mean daily rate and its mean error? $+ 0^s.82; \; 0^s.042.$

9. If the error of a single measurement of an angle by a repeating circle consists of parts due to sighting and reading respectively, so that

$$r^2 = r_1^2 + r_2^2,$$

show that the probable error when the angle is repeated n times is

$$\sqrt{\left(\frac{r_1^2}{n} + \frac{r_2^2}{n^2}\right)}.$$

10. If the measured sides of a rectangle have the same probable error, show that the diagonal is determined with the same precision as either side.

11. The compression of the earth's meridian was found to be $\frac{1}{294}$, with a probable error of .000046; what is the probable error of the denominator 294?   3.98.

12. When a line whose length is l is measured by the repeated application of a unit of measure, show that its probable error is of the form

$$R = r\sqrt{l}.$$

13. What is the probable error of the area of the rectangle whose sides measured as in the preceding example are z_1 and z_2?

$$r\sqrt{[z_1 z_2 (z_1 + z_2)]}.$$

14. A line of levels is run in the following manner: the back and fore sights are taken at distances of about 200 feet, so that there are thirteen stations per mile, and at each sight the rod is read three times. If the probable error of a single reading is 0.01 of a foot, what is the probable error of the difference of level of two points which are ten miles apart?   .093.

15. Show that the probable error of the weighted mean of observed quantities has its least possible value when the weights are inversely proportional to the squares of the probable errors of the quantities, and that this value is the same as that given in Art. 68 for the case of observed value of the same quantity.

VII.

The Combination of Independent Determinations of the Same Quantity.

The Distinction between Precision and Accuracy.

92. We have seen in Arts. 63 and 67 that the final determination of the observed quantity derived from a set of observations follows the exponential law of the facility of accidental errors. The discrepancies of the observations have given us the means of determining a measure of the risk of error in the single observations, and we have found that the like measure for the final determination varies inversely as the square root of its weight compared with that of the single observation. Since this weight increases directly with the number of constituent observations, it is thus possible to diminish the risk of error indefinitely; in other words, to increase without limit the *precision* of our final result.

93. It is important to notice, however, that this is by no means the same thing as to say that it is possible by multiplying the number of observations to increase without limit the *accuracy* of the result. The precision of a determination has to do only with the accidental errors; so that the diminution of the probable error, while it indicates the reduction of the risk of such errors, gives no indication of the *systematic** errors (see Art. 3)

---

* The term systematic is sometimes applied to errors produced by a cause operating in a systematic manner upon the several observations, thus producing discrepancies obviously not following the law of accidental errors. Usually a discussion of these errors leads to the discovery of their cause, and ultimately to the corrections by means of which they may be removed. All the remaining errors, whose causes are unknown, are generally spoken of as accidental errors ; but in this book the term accidental is applied only to those errors which are variable in the system of observations under consideration, as distinguished from those which have a common value for the entire system.

which are produced by unknown causes affecting all the observations of the system to exactly the same extent.

The value to which we approach indefinitely as the precision of the determination is increased has hitherto been spoken of as the "true value," but it is more properly *the precise value* corresponding to the instrument or method of observation employed. Since the systematic error is common to the whole system of observations, it is evident that it will enter into the final result unchanged, no matter what may be the number of observations; whereas the object of increasing this number is to allow the accidental errors to destroy one another. Thus the systematic error is the difference between the precise value, from which accidental errors are supposed to be entirely eliminated, and the accurate or true value of the quantity sought.

94. Hence, when in Art. 64 the arithmetical mean of n observations was compared to an observation made with a more precise instrument, it is important to notice that this new instrument must be imagined to lead to the same ultimate precise value, that is, it must have the same systematic error as the actual instrument, whereas in practice a new instrument might have a very different systematic error.

Again, in the illustration employed in Art. 64, where the final determination of an angle is given as $36° 42'.3 \pm 1'.22$, the "true value," which is just as likely as not to lie between the limits thus assigned, is only the true value so far as the instrument and method employed can give it; that is, the precise value to which the determination would approach if its weight were increased indefinitely.

95. A failure to appreciate the distinction drawn in the preceding articles may lead to a false estimate of the value of the method of Least Squares. M. Faye in his "Cours d'Astronomie" gives the following example of the objections which have been urged against the method: "From the discussion of the transits of Venus observed in 1761 and 1769, M. Encke deduced for the parallax of the sun the value

$$8''.57116 \pm 0''.0370.$$

In accordance with this small probable error it would be a wager of one to one that the true parallax is comprised between $8''.53$ and $8''.61$. Now we know to-day that the true parallax $8''.813$ falls far outside of these limits. The error, $0''.24184$, is equal to 6.536 times the probable error $0''.037$. We find for the probability of such an error 0.00001. Hence, adhering to the probable error assigned by M. Encke to his result, one could wager a hundred thousand to one that it is not in error by 0.24184, and nevertheless such is the correction which we are obliged to make it undergo."

Of course, as M. Faye remarks, astronomers can now point out many of the errors for which proper corrections were not made; but the important thing to notice is that, even in Encke's time, the wagers cited above were not authorized by the theory. The value of the parallax assigned by Encke was the most probable with the evidence then known, and it was an even wager that the complete elimination of errors of the kind that produced the discrepancies or contradictions among the observations could not carry the result beyond the limit assigned; but the existence of other unknown causes of error and the probable amount of inaccuracy resulting from them is quite a different question.

Relative Accidental and Systematic Errors.

96. Let us now suppose that two determinations of a quantity have been made with the same instrument and by the same method, so that they have the same systematic error, if any; in other words, they correspond to the same precise value. The difference between the two results is the algebraic difference between the accidental errors remaining in the two determinations; this may be called their *relative accidental error*. Regarding the two determinations as independent measurements of two quantities, if r_1 and r_2 are their probable errors, that of their difference is $\sqrt{(r_1^2 + r_2^2)}$; and, since this difference should be zero, the relative error is an error in a system for which the probable error is

$$r = \sqrt{(r_1^2 + r_2^2)}.$$

For example, if the determination of an angle mentioned in Art. 94 is the mean of ten observations, it is an even wager that the mean of ten more observations of the same kind shall differ from $36° \, 42'.3$ by an amount not exceeding $1'.22 \times \sqrt{2}$ or $1'.73$. Again, r being the probable error of a single observation, the probable error of the mean of n observations is $\dfrac{r}{\sqrt{n}}$, but the discrepancy from this mean of a new single observation is as likely as not to exceed

$$\sqrt{\left(\frac{r^2}{n} + r^2 \right)}, \quad \text{that is,} \quad r\sqrt{\frac{n+1}{n}}.^*$$

97. If, on the other hand, the two determinations have been made with different instruments or by a different method, they may involve different systematic errors; so that, if each determination were made perfectly precise, they would still differ by an amount equal to the algebraic difference of their systematic errors. Let this difference, which may be called the *relative systematic error*, be denoted by δ. Then, d denoting the actual difference of the two determinations, while δ is the difference between the corresponding precise values, we may put

$$d = \delta + x,$$

in which x is the relative accidental error.

The Relative Weights of Independent Determinations.

98. In combining values to obtain a final mean value, we have hitherto supposed their relative weights to be known or assumed beforehand, as in Arts. 75 and 77. Since the squares of the probable errors are inversely proportional to the weights, (Arts. 66 and 68,) the ratios of the probable errors both of the constituents and of the mean are thus known in advance, and it

---

* This does not apply to the residuals of the original n observations, because in taking a residual the mean is not independent of the single observation with which it is compared.

only remains to determine a single absolute value of a probable error to fix them all. In this process it is assumed that the values have all the same systematic error.

But, when the determinations are independently made, their relative weights are not known, and their probable errors have to be found independently. If now it can be assumed that the systematic errors are the same, so that there is no relative systematic error, the weights may be taken in the inverse ratio of the squares of the probable errors.

99. To determine whether the above assumption can fairly be made in the case of two independent determinations whose probable errors are r_1 and r_2, it is necessary to compare the difference d with the relative probable error $\sqrt{(r_1^2 + r_2^2)}$, Art. 96. If d is small enough to be regarded as a relative accidental error, it is safe to make the assumption and combine the determinations in the manner mentioned above.

As an example, let us suppose that a certain angle has been determined by a theodolite as

$$24° \ 13' \ 36'' \pm 3''.1,$$

and that a second determination made with a surveyor's transit is

$$24° \ 13' \ 24'' \pm 13''.8.$$

In this case $r_1 = 3.1$, $r_2 = 13.8$ and $d = 12$. It is obvious that a relative accidental error as great as d may reasonably be expected. (In fact the relative probable error is 14.1 ; and, by Table II, the chance that the accidental error should be at least as great as 12 is about .57.) We may therefore assume that there is no relative systematic error, and combine the determinations with weights having the inverse ratio of the squares of the probable errors. This ratio will be found, in the present case, to be about 20 : 1, and the corresponding weighted mean found by adding $\frac{1}{21}$ of the difference to the first value, is

$$24° \ 13' \ 35''.43.$$

100. It appears doubtful at first that the value given by the theodolite can be improved by combining with it the value given by the inferior instrument. The propriety of the above process becomes more apparent, however, if we imagine the first determination to be the mean of twenty observations made with the theodolite; a single one of these observations will then have the same weight and the same probable error as the second determination. Now the discrepancy of this new determination from the mean is such as we may expect to find in a new single observation with the theodolite. We are therefore justified in treating it as such an observation, and taking the mean of the twenty-one supposed observations for our final result.

101. The probable error of the result found in Art. 99 of course corresponds with its weight; thus, denoting it by R, we have $R^2 = \frac{20}{21} r_1^2$, whence $R = 3''.03$, and the final result is

$$24° \; 13' \; 35''.43 \pm 3''.03.$$

In general, r_1 and r_2 being the given probable errors, that of the mean is given by

$$R^2 = \frac{r_1^2 r_2^2}{r_1^2 + r_2^2}.$$

Determinations which, considering their probable errors, are in sufficient agreement to be treated as in the foregoing articles may be called *concordant determinations*. They correspond to the same precise value of the observed quantity, and the result of their combination is to be regarded as a better determination of the same precise value.

The Combination of Discordant Determinations.

102. As a second illustration of determinations independently made, let us suppose that a determination of the zenith distance of a star made at one culmination is

$$14° \; 53' \; 12''.1 \pm 0''.3,$$

and that at another culmination we find for the same quantity

$$14° \; 53' \; 14''.3 \pm 0''.5.$$

In this case we have $d = 2.2$. This is about 3.8 times the relative probable error whose value is $0''.58$.

From Table II we find that the probability that the relative accidental error should be as great as d is only about 1 in 100. We are therefore justified in assuming that the difference d is mainly due to errors peculiar to the culminations. In other words, we assume that, could we have obtained the precise values corresponding to the two culminations, (by indefinitely increasing the number of observations at each,) they would still be found to differ by about $2''.2$. Supposing now that there is no reason for preferring one of these precise values to the other, we ought to take their simple arithmetical mean for the final result; and, since the two given values are comparatively close to the precise values in question, we may take their arithmetical mean, which is

$$14° \ 53' \ 13''.2,$$

for the final determination.

103. Determinations like those considered above, whose difference is so great as to indicate an actual difference between the precise values to which they tend, may be called *discordant determinations.* The discordance of the two determinations discloses the existence of systematic errors which were not indicated by the discrepancies of the observations upon which the given probable errors were based. In combining the determinations, these systematic errors are treated as accidental errors incident to the two determinations considered as two observed values of the required quantity. In fact, it is generally the object in making new and independent determinations to eliminate as far as possible a new class of errors by bringing them into the category of accidental errors which tend to neutralize each other in the final result. The probable error of the result cannot now be derived from the given probable errors, but must be inferred from the determinations themselves considered as observed values, because we now take cognizance of errors which are not indicated by the given probable errors.

104. When there are but two observed values, formula (4), Art. 72, becomes

$$R_0 = \rho \sqrt{2} \sqrt{\frac{p_1 v_1^2 + p_2 v_2^2}{p_1 + p_2}},$$

in which p_1, p_2 are the weights assigned to the two values. Denoting the difference by d, the residuals have opposite signs, and their absolute values are

$$v_1 = \frac{p_2}{p_1 + p_2} d, \qquad v_2 = \frac{p_1}{p_1 + p_2} d.$$

Substituting these values, we have for the probable error of the mean

$$R_0 = \rho \frac{\sqrt{(2p_1 p_2)}}{p_1 + p_2} d \ 0.6745 \frac{\sqrt{(p_1 p_2)}}{p_1 + p_2} d \ . \ . \ . \ (1)$$

When $p_1 = p_2$, this becomes

$$R_0 = \frac{\rho d}{\sqrt{2}} = 0.3372\, d. \ . \ . \ . \ . \ . \ (2)$$

In the example given in Art. 102, the value of R_0 thus obtained is $0''.742$, which, owing to the discordance of the two given determinations, considerably exceeds each of the given probable errors.

Of course no great confidence can be placed in the results given by the formulæ above on account of the small value of n.*

105. Since the error of each determination is the sum of its accidental and systematic error, if s_1 and s_2 denote the probable

---

* The argument by which it is shown that the value of h deduced in Art. 69 is the most probable value involves the assumption that before the observations were made all values of h are to be regarded as equally probable; just as that by which it is shown that the arithmetical mean is the most probable value of the observed quantity a involves the assumption that before the observations all values of a were equally probable. In the case of a, the assumption is admissible with respect to all values of a which can possibly come in question. But, in the case of h, this is not true; because (supposing $n = 2$ as above) when $d = 0$ the value of h is infinite, and when d is small the corresponding values of h are very large, so that it is impossible to admit that all values of h which can arise are à *priori* equally probable.

In the present application of the formula, however, these inadmissible values do not arise, because we do not use it when d is small, employing instead the method of Art. 99 and the formula of Art. 101.

systematic errors, the probable errors of the two determinations when both classes of errors are considered are

$$R_1 = \sqrt{(r_1^2 + s_1^2)}, \qquad R_2 = \sqrt{(r_2^2 + s_2^2)}.$$

The proper ratio of weights with which the determinations should be combined is $R_2^2 : R_1^2$. The method of procedure followed in Art. 99 assumes that s_1 and s_2 vanish. On the other hand, in the process employed in Art. 102 we are guided, in an assumption of the ratio $R_2^2 : R_1^2$, by a consideration of the value which the ratio $s_2^2 : s_1^2$ ought to have.

For example, in the illustration, Art. 102, the ratio $R_2^2 : R_1^2$ is taken to be one of equality, whereas the hypothesis we desired to make was that $s_1 = s_2$, so that we ought to have

$$R_1^2 - R_2^2 = r_1^2 - r_2^2.$$

On the hypothesis $R_1 = R_2$ the value of each of these probable errors is, in accordance with equation (2), Art. 104, ρd. In the example this is $1''.05$. If we take $(1.05)^2$ as the average value of R_1^2 and R_2^2, and introduce the condition written above, we shall find as a second approximation to the value of the ratio $R_2^2 : R_1^2$ about $15 : 13$. The final value corresponding to this ratio of weights is $14° 53' 13''.1$, and its probable error as determined by equation (1), Art. 104, is slightly less than that before found, namely, $R_0 = 0''.740$.

Indicated and Concealed Portions of the Risk of Error.

106. It will be convenient in the following articles to speak of the square of the probable error as the measure of the risk of error.

The foregoing discussion shows that the total risk of error, R^2, of any determination consists of two parts, r^2 and s^2, of which the first only is indicated by discrepancies among the observations of which the given determination is the mean. It is only this first part that can be diminished by increasing the number of the constituent observations. The remaining part remains concealed, and cannot be diminished until some variation is made in the circumstances under which the observations are made, giving rise to new determinations. When the indicated portions of the risk of error in the several determinations are sufficiently diminished, discordance between them must always be expected, and this discordance brings into evidence a new portion, but still it may be only a portion, of the hitherto concealed part of the risk of error.

107. What we have called in Art. 103 discordant determinations are those in which the indication of this new portion of the risk of error, to which corresponds the relative systematic error, is unmistakable, because of its magnitude in comparison with what remains of the portion first indicated in the separate determinations, that is, r_1^2 and r_2^2. On the other hand, the concordant determinations of Art. 101 are those in which the new portion is so small compared with r_1^2 and r_2^2 as to remain concealed.

Thus, to return to the illustration discussed in Art. 99, if twenty times as many observations had been involved in the determination by the transit, its probable error would have been reduced to equality with that of the determination by the theodolite. But if this had been done we should almost certainly have found the determinations discordant ; that is to say, the ratio in which the difference between the determinations is reduced would be much less than that in which the probable relative accidental error $\sqrt{(r_1^2 + r_2^2)}$ is diminished. The ratio in which the remaining difference between the determinations should be divided in making the final determination now depends upon our estimate of the comparative freedom of the instruments from systematic error,* but the important thing to be noted is that the probable error of the result would now be found as in Art. 104, and would be greater than those of the

---

*It may be assumed that, when the instruments are carefully adjusted, the one which is less liable to accidental errors is correspondingly less liable to systematic errors. But this comparison is concerned with the probable errors *of a single observation* in each case, and not with those of the determinations themselves.

separate determinations.   Thus the *apparent* risk of error would be increased by making a new determination, but this is only because a greater part of the total risk of error has been made apparent, and the result is so much the more trustworthy as a greater variety has been introduced into the methods employed.

The Total Probable Error of a Determination.

108. In the illustrations given in Arts. 99 and 102 it was supposed that two determinations only were made, so that we had but a single discrepancy upon which to base our judgment of the probable amount of the relative systematic error. But, in general, what are regarded as determinations at one stage of the process are at the next stage treated as observations which may be repeated indefinitely before being combined into a new determination.   Let one of the determinations first made be the mean of n observations equally good, and let r be the probable error of a single observation.   Then the probable accidental error of the mean is $r_0 = \dfrac{r}{\sqrt{n}}$.   Now, if R is the probable error of the final value as obtained directly from the discrepancies of the several determinations, (their number being supposed great enough to allow us to obtain a trustworthy value,) we shall find that R exceeds r_0, and putting

$$R^2 = \frac{r^2}{n} + r_1^2, \quad \cdots \quad \cdots \quad (1)$$

r_1^2 is the new portion of the risk of error brought out by the comparison of the determinations.

109. The form of this equation shows that when $\dfrac{r^2}{n}$ is already small compared with r_1^2, the advantage gained by increasing the value of n soon becomes inappreciable.

For example, the reticule of a meridian circle is provided with a number of threads, in order that several observations of time may be taken at a single transit.   If seven equidistant threads are used, the mean of the times is equivalent to a determination based upon seven observations of the time of transit. Chauvenet found that, for moderately skilful observers, the probable accidental error of the transit over a single thread of an equatorial star is $r = 0^s.08$, whence for the mean of the seven threads we have $r_0 = 0^s.03$. The probable error of a single determination of the right ascension of an equatorial star was found to be $R = 0^s.06$, so that, from $R^2 = r_0^2 + r_1^2$ we have $r_1 = 0^s.052$. The conclusion is reached that "an increase of the number of threads would be attended by no important advantage," and it is stated that Bessel thought five threads sufficient.*

110. Suppose the value of R^2 in equation (1), Art. 108, to have been derived from the discrepancies of n' determinations of equal weight. A systematic error may exist for these n' determinations, and s_1 being its probable value, we shall have

$$s^2 = r_1^2 + s_1^2,$$

that is to say, the concealed portion of the risk of error in one of the original determinations has been decomposed into two parts, one of which has been disclosed at the second stage of the process, while the other remains concealed.

The total risk of error in a single one of the n' determinations is $R^2 + s_1^2$, and that of the mean of the determinations is $\dfrac{R^2}{n'} + s_1^2$.

In like manner, if at a further stage of the process we have the means of finding the value of the probable error R_1 of this new determination by direct comparison with other coordinate determinations, a portion of the value of s_1^2 will be disclosed, and we shall have

$$R_1^2 = \frac{R^2}{n'} + r_2^2 = \frac{r^2}{nn'} + \frac{r_1^2}{n'} + r_2^2,$$

where again it must be supposed that a portion s_2^2 of the risk of error still remains concealed.

---

* Chauvenet's "Spherical and Practical Astronomy," vol. ii, p. 194 et seq.

III. The comparative amounts of the risk of error which are disclosed at the various stages of the process depend upon the amount of variety introduced into the method of observing. Thus, to resume the illustration given in Art. 109, if the star be observed at n' culminations, r^2 will correspond to errors peculiar to a thread, and r_1^2 will correspond to errors peculiar to a culmination. Again, if different stars whose right ascensions are known are observed, in order to obtain the local sidereal time used in a determination of the longitude, r_2^2 will correspond to errors peculiar to a star, together with instrumental errors peculiar to the meridian altitude.

The Ultimate Limit of Accuracy.

112. The considerations adduced in the preceding articles seem to point to the conclusion that there must always be a residuum of the risk of error that has not yet been reached, and thus to explain the apparent existence " of an ultimate limit of accuracy beyond which no mass of accumulated observations can ever penetrate."* But it does not appear to be necessary to suppose, as done by Professor Peirce, that there is an absolute fixed limit of accuracy, due to " a failure of the law of error embodied in the method of Least Squares, when it is extended to minute errors." He says : " In approaching the ultimate limit of accuracy, the probable error ceases to diminish proportionally to the increase of the number of observations, so that the accuracy of the mean of several determinations does not surpass that of the single determinations as much as it should do, in conformity with the law of least squares ; thus it appears that the probable error of the mean of the determinations of the longitude of the Harvard Observatory, deduced from the moon-culminating observations of 1845, 1846, and 1847, is $1^s.28$ instead of $1^s.00$, to which it should have been reduced conformably to the accuracy of the separate determinations of those years."

---

* Prof. Benjamin Peirce, *U. S. Coast Survey Report* for 1854, Appendix, p. 109.

To account for the fact cited on the principles laid down above, it is only necessary to suppose that there are causes of error which have varied from year to year; and, recognizing this fact, we ought to obtain our final determination by comparing the determinations of a number of years, and not by combining into one result the whole mass of observations.

Examples.

1. In a system of observations equally good, r being the probable error of a single observation, if two observations are selected at random, what quantity is their difference as likely as not to exceed? $r \sqrt{2}$.

2. In example 1, what is the probability that the difference shall be less than r? 0.367.

3. When two determinations are made by the same method, show that the odds are in favor of a difference less than the sum of the two probable errors, and against a difference less than the greater of the two, and find the extreme values of these odds.

66 : 34 and 63 : 37.

4. A and B observe the same angle repeatedly with the same instrument, with the following results:

A	B
47° 23′ 40″	47° 23′ 30″
47 23 45	47 23 40
47 23 30	47 23 50
47 23 35	47 24 00
47 23 40	47 23 20

Show that there is no evidence of relative systematic (personal) error. Find the relative weights of an observation by A and by B, and the final determination of the angle.

100 : 13; 47° 23′ 38″.23 ± 1″.62.

5. Show that the probable error in example 4 as computed from the ten observations taken with their proper weights is 1″.53, but that derived from the formula of Art. 104 is 0″.43, which is much too small. (See foot-note, p. 83.)

6. Two determinations of the length of a line in feet give respectively 683.4 ± 0.3 and 684.9 ± 0.3, there being no reason for preferring one of the corresponding precise values to the other; show that the probable error of each of the precise values (that is, the systematic error of each determination) is 0.65; and that the best final determination is 684.15 ± 0.51.

7. Show generally that when the weights are inversely proportional to the squares of the probable errors, the formula of Art. 104 gives a value of R greater or less than that given by the formula of Art. 101, according as d is greater or less than the relative mean error.

VIII.

Observation Equations.

113. We have considered the case in which a quantity whose value is to be determined is directly observed, or is expressed as a function of quantities directly observed. We come now to that in which the quantity sought is one of a number of unknown quantities of which those directly observed are functions. The equation expressing that a known function of several unknown quantities has a certain observed value is called an *observation equation*. Let μ denote the number of unknown quantities concerned. Then, in order to determine them, we must have at least μ independent equations. Thus, if two of the equations express observed values of the same function of the unknown quantities, they will either be identical, so that we have in effect only $\mu - 1$ equations, or else they will be inconsistent, so that the values of the unknown quantities will be impossible. So also it must not be possible to derive any one of the μ equations, or one differing from it only in the absolute term, from two or more of the other equations.

114. If we have no more than the necessary μ equations, we shall have no indication of the precision with which the observations have been made, nor, consequently, any measure of the precision with which the unknown quantities have been determined. With respect to them, we are in the same condition as when a single observed value is given in the case of direct observations.

Now let other observation equations be given, that is to say, let the values of other functions* of the unknown quantities be observed. The results of substituting the values of the unknown

---

* It is not necessary that these additional equations should be independent of the original μ equations, for an equation expressing a new observed value of a function already observed will be useful in determining the precision of the observations.

quantities will, owing to the errors of observation, be found to differ from the observed values, and the discrepancies will give an indication of the precision of the observations, just as the discrepancies between observed values of the same quantity do, in the case of direct observations.

115. As an example, let us take the following four observation equations* involving x, y and z:

$$x - y + 2z = 3,$$
$$3x + 2y - 5z = 5,$$
$$4x + y + 4z = 21,$$
$$-x + 3y + 3z = 14.$$

If we solve the first three equations we shall find

$$x = 2\tfrac{4}{7}, \qquad y = 3\tfrac{2}{7}, \qquad z = 1\tfrac{6}{7}.$$

Substituting these values in the fourth equation, the value of the first member is $12\tfrac{6}{7}$, whereas the observed value is 14; the discrepancy is $1\tfrac{1}{7}$. If the values above were the true values, the errors of observation committed must have been $0, 0, 0, 1\tfrac{1}{7}$; but, since each of the observed quantities is liable to error, this is not a likely system of errors to have been committed. In fact, any system of values we may assign to x, y and z implies a system of errors in the observed quantities, and the most probable system of values is that to which corresponds the most probable system of errors.

116. In general, let there be m observation equations, involving μ unknown quantities, $m > \mu$; then we have first to consider the mode of deriving from them the most probable values of the unknown quantities. The system of errors in the observed quantities which this system of values implies will then enable us to measure the precision of the observations. Finally, regarding the μ unknown quantities as functions of the m observed quantities, we shall obtain for each unknown quantity a measure of the precision with which it has been determined.

---

* Gauss, " Theoria Motus Corporum Coelestium," Art. 184.

The Reduction of Observation Equations to the Linear Form.

117. The method of obtaining the values of the unknown quantities, to which we proceed, requires that the observation equations should be linear. When this is not the case, it is necessary to employ approximately equivalent linear equations, which are obtained in the following manner.

Let X, Y, Z, ... be the unknown quantities, and M_1, M_2, ... M_m the observed quantities; the observation equations are then of the form

$$f_1(X, Y, Z, \ldots) = M_1,$$
$$f_2(X, Y, Z, \ldots) = M_2,$$
$$\cdot \quad \cdot \quad \cdot \quad \cdot \quad \cdot \quad \cdot \quad \cdot \quad \cdot$$
$$f_m(X, Y, Z, \ldots) = M_m,$$

where $f_1, f_2, \ldots f_m$ are known functions. Let X_0, Y_0, Z_0, ... be approximate values of X, Y, Z, ..., which, if not otherwise known, may be found by solving μ of the equations; and put

$$X = X_0 + x, \qquad Y = Y_0 + y, \quad \ldots,$$

so that x, y, z, ... are small corrections to be applied to the approximate values. Then the first observation equation may be written

$$f_1(X_0 + x, \ Y_0 + y, \ Z_0 + z, \ldots) = M_1,$$

or, expanding by Taylor's theorem,

$$f_1(X_0, Y_0, Z_0, \ldots) + \frac{df_1}{dX_0} x + \frac{df_1}{dY_0} y + \frac{df_1}{dZ_0} z + \ldots = M_1,$$

where the coefficients of x, y, z, ... are the values which the partial derivatives of $f_1(X, Y, Z, \ldots)$ assume when $X = X_0$, $Y = Y_0$, $Z = Z_0$, ..., and the powers and products of the small quantities x, y, z, ... are neglected as in Art. 91.

Denoting the coefficients of x, y, z, ... by a_1, b_1, c_1, ..., putting n_1 for $M_1 - f_1(X_0, Y_0, Z_0, \ldots)$, and treating the other observation equations in the same way, we may write

$$\left.\begin{array}{l} a_1x + b_1y + c_1z + \ldots = n_1 \\ a_2x + b_2y + c_2z + \ldots = n_2 \\ \cdot \quad \cdot \quad \cdot \quad \cdot \quad \cdot \quad \cdot \quad \cdot \quad \cdot \\ a_mx + b_my + c_mz + \ldots = n_m \end{array}\right\}, \quad \cdots \quad (\text{I})$$

for the observation equations in their linear form.

118. Even when the original observation equations are in the linear form, it is generally best to transform them as above, so that the values of the unknown quantities shall be small.

Another transformation sometimes made consists in replacing one of the unknown quantities by a fixed multiple of it. For example, if the values of the coefficients of y are inconveniently large they may be reduced in value by substituting ky' for y and giving to k a suitably small value.

119. In the observation equations (1), the second members may be regarded as the observed quantities, since they have the same errors. If the true values of $x, y, z, \ldots$ are substituted in these equations they will not be satisfied, because each n differs from its proper value by the error of observation v; we may therefore write the equations

$$\left.\begin{array}{l} a_1x + b_1y + c_1z + \ldots - n_1 = v_1 \\ a_2x + b_2y + c_2z + \ldots - n_2 = v_2 \\ \cdot \quad \cdot \quad \cdot \quad \cdot \quad \cdot \quad \cdot \quad \cdot \quad \cdot \\ a_mx + b_my + c_mz + \ldots - n_m = v_m \end{array}\right\}, \quad \cdots \quad (2)$$

in which, if $x, y, z, \ldots$ are the true values, $v_1, v_2, \ldots v_m$ are the true errors of observation, and if any set of values be given to $x, y, z, \ldots$, the second members are the corresponding *residuals*. These corrected observation equations may be called the *residual equations*.

Observation Equations of Equal Precision.

120. Let us first suppose that the m observations are equally good, and let h be their common measure of precision. Then, since v is the error, not only of the absolute term n_1 in the first of equations (2), but of the first observed quantity M_1, the probability before the observations are made that the first observed value shall be M_1 is

$$\frac{h}{\sqrt{\pi}}\, e^{-h^2 v_1^2}\, \Delta v,$$

where, as in Art. 35, Δv is the least count of the instrument. Hence we have, for the probability before the observations are made that the m actual observed values shall occur,

$$P = \frac{h^m}{\pi^{\frac{1}{2}m}}\, e^{-h^2(v_1^2 + v_2^2 + \cdots v_m^2)}\, \Delta v^m,$$

exactly as in Art. 41. The values of v_1^2, v_2^2, ... v_m^2 being given by equations (2), this value of P is a function of the several unknown quantities; hence it follows, as in Art. 41, that for any one of them that value is, after the observations have been made, most probable which assigns to P its maximum value; in other words, that value which makes

$$v_1^2 + v_2^2 + \ldots + v_m^2 = \text{a minimum.}$$

Thus the principle of Least Squares applies to indirect as well as to direct observations.

121. To determine the most probable value of x, we have, by differentiation with respect to x,

$$v_1\, \frac{dv_1}{dx} + v_2\, \frac{dv_2}{dx} + \ldots + v_m\, \frac{dv_m}{dx} = 0,$$

or, since, from equations (2), Art. 119,

$$\frac{dv_1}{dx} = a_1, \quad \frac{dv_2}{dx} = a_2, \quad \ldots \quad \frac{dv_n}{dx} = a_n,$$

$$a_1 v_1 + a_2 v_2 + \ldots + a_m v_m = 0. \quad \ldots \quad \ldots \quad (1)$$

This is called the *normal equation for x*. Whatever values are assigned to y, z, ..., it gives the rule for determining the value of x which is most probable on the hypothesis that the values assigned to the other unknown quantities are correct.

Since v_1, v_2, ... v_m represent the first members of the observation equations (1), Art. 117, when so written that the second member is zero, we see that *the normal equation for x may be formed by multiplying each observation equation by the coefficient of x in it, and adding the results.*

122. The rule just given for forming the normal equation shows it to be a linear combination of the observation equations, and the reason why the multipliers should be as stated may be further explained as follows: If we suppose fixed values given to $y, z, \ldots$, each observation equation may be written in the form $ax = N$, where N only differs from the observed value M by a fixed quantity, and therefore has the same probable error. Now, writing the observation equations in the form

$$x = \frac{N_1}{a_1} = x_1,$$

$$x = \frac{N_2}{a_2} = x_2,$$

$$\cdot \quad \cdot \quad \cdot \quad \cdot \quad \cdot \quad \cdot$$

$$x = \frac{N_m}{a_m} = x_m,$$

we may regard them as expressing direct observations of x. If r is the common probable error of $N_1, N_2, \ldots N_m$, that of $\frac{N_1}{a_1}$ or x_1 is $\frac{r}{a_1}$; that of x_2 is $\frac{r}{a_2}$, and so on. Thus the equations are not of equal precision for determining x, and their weights when written as above (being inversely as the squares of the probable errors) are as $a_1^2 : a_2^2 : \ldots : a_m^2$. It follows that the equation for finding x is, as in the case of the weighted arithmetical mean (see Art. 66), the result of adding the above equations multiplied respectively by $a_1^2, a_2^2, \ldots a_m^2$;* that is to say, it is the result of adding the original observation equations of the form $ax - N = 0$ multiplied respectively by $a_1, a_2, \ldots a_m$.

---

*It must not be assumed that the weight of the value of x, determined from the several normal equations, is Σa^2, that of an observation being unity. This is its weight only upon the supposition that the absolute values of the other quantities are known.

The Normal Equations.

123. In like manner, for each of the other unknown quantities we can form a normal equation, and we thus have a system of equations whose number is equal to that of the unknown quantities. The solution of this system of normal equations gives the most probable values of the unknown quantities. Let us take for example the four observation equations given in Art. 115. Forming the normal equations by the rule given above, we have

$$27x + 6y \qquad = 88,$$
$$6x + 15y + z = 70,$$
$$y + 54z = 107.$$

The solution of this system of equations gives for the most probable values,

$$x = \frac{49154}{19899} = 2.47,$$
$$y = \frac{2617}{737} = 3.55,$$
$$z = \frac{12707}{6633} = 1.92.$$

124. Writing the observation equations in their general form,

$$\left. \begin{aligned} a_1x + b_1y + \ldots + l_1t = n_1 \\ a_2x + b_2y + \ldots + l_2t = n_2 \\ \cdots \cdots \cdots \cdots \cdots \cdots \cdots \\ a_mx + b_my + \ldots + l_mt = n_m \end{aligned} \right\}, \quad \ldots \quad (1)$$

we obtain for the normal equations in their general form,

$$\left. \begin{aligned} \Sigma a^2 . x + \Sigma ab . y + \ldots + \Sigma al . t = \Sigma an \\ \Sigma ab . x + \Sigma b^2 . y + \ldots + \Sigma bl . t = \Sigma bn \\ \cdots \cdots \cdots \cdots \cdots \cdots \cdots \cdots \\ \Sigma al . x + \Sigma bl . y + \ldots + \Sigma l^2 . t = \Sigma ln \end{aligned} \right\} \ldots \quad (2)$$

It will be noticed that the coefficient of the rth unknown quantity in the sth equation is the same as that of the sth unknown quantity in the rth equation; in other words, the determinant of the coefficients of the unknown quantities in equations (2) is a symmetrical one.

Observation Equations of Unequal Precision.

125. When the observations are not equally good, if

$$h_1, h_2, \ldots h_m$$

are the measures of precision of the observed values

$$M_1, M_2, \ldots M_m,$$

the expression to be made a minimum is

$$h_1^2 v_1^2 + h_2^2 v_2^2 + \ldots + h_m^2 v_m^2,$$

as in Art. 65. Thus, as in the case of direct observations, if the error of each observation be multiplied by its measure of precision so as to reduce the errors to the same relative value, *it is necessary that the sum of the squares of the reduced errors should be a minimum.*

Since $v_1 = 0, v_2 = 0, \ldots v_m = 0$ are equivalent to the observation equations, it follows that, if we multiply each observation equation by its measure of precision (so that it takes the form $hv = 0$), we may regard the results as equations of equal precision.

126. The result may be otherwise expressed by using numbers $p_1, p_2, \ldots p_m$ proportional, as in Art. 66, to the squares of the measures of precision; the quantity to be made a minimum then is

$$p_1 v_1^2 + p_2 v_2^2 + \ldots + p_m v_m^2,$$

and the normal equation for x is

$$p_1 a_1 v_1 + p_2 a_2 v_2 + \ldots + p_m a_m v_m = 0.$$

The numbers $p_1, p_2, \ldots p_m$ are called the weights of the observation equations; thus, in the case of weighted equations, *the normal equation for x may be formed by multiplying each observation equation by the coefficient of x in it, and also by its weight, and adding the results.*

The general form of the normal equations is now

$$\left.\begin{array}{l}
\Sigma pa^2 . x + \Sigma pab . y + \ldots + \Sigma pal . t = \Sigma pan \\
\Sigma pab . x + \Sigma pb^2 . y + \ldots + \Sigma pbl . t = \Sigma pbn \\
\cdots \cdots \cdots \cdots \cdots \cdots \cdots \cdots \\
\Sigma pal . x + \Sigma pbl . y + \ldots + \Sigma pl^2 . t = \Sigma pln
\end{array}\right\} \quad . \quad . \ (3)$$

The result is evidently the same as if each observation equation had been first multiplied by the square root of its weight, by which means it would be reduced to the weight unity, and the system would take the form (2), Art. 124.

Formation of the Normal Equations.

127. When the normal equations are calculated by means of their general form, a table of squares is useful not only in calculating the coefficients Σpa^2, Σpb^2, ... Σpl^2, but also in the case of those of the form Σpab, Σpac, ... Σpan, ... For, since

$$ab = \tfrac{1}{2}[(a + b)^2 - a^2 - b^2],$$

we have

$$\Sigma pab = \tfrac{1}{2}[\Sigma p(a + b)^2 - \Sigma pa^2 - \Sigma pb^2],$$

by means of which Σpab is expressed in terms of squares.* Or for the same purpose we may use

$$\Sigma pab = \tfrac{1}{2}[\Sigma pa^2 + \Sigma pb^2 - \Sigma p(a - b)^2].$$

In performing the work it is convenient to arrange the coefficients in a tabular form in the order in which they occur in the observation equations, and, adding a column containing the sums of the coefficients in each equation, thus,

$$s_1 = a_1 + b_1 + \ldots + l_1 + n_1, \quad \text{etc.,}$$

---

* If Σpab alone were to be found, the formula

$$\Sigma pab = \tfrac{1}{4}[\Sigma p(a + b)^2 - \Sigma p(a - b)^2],$$

derived from that of quarter-squares, would be preferable; but, since Σpa^2, Σpb^2 have also to be calculated, the use of the formula above, which was suggested by Bessel, involves less additional labor.

to form the quantities Σpas, Σpbs, ... Σpns in addition to those which occur in the normal equations. We ought then to find

$$\Sigma pas = \Sigma pa^2 + \Sigma pab + \ldots + \Sigma pan,$$
$$\Sigma pbs = \Sigma pab + \Sigma pb^2 + \ldots + \Sigma pbn,$$
$$\cdot \quad \cdot \quad \cdot \quad \cdot \quad \cdot \quad \cdot \quad \cdot \quad \cdot \quad \cdot \quad \cdot \quad \cdot$$
$$\Sigma pns = \Sigma pan + \Sigma pbn + \ldots + \Sigma pn^2,$$

and the fulfilment of these conditions is a verification of the accuracy of the work.

In many cases, the use of logarithms is to be preferred, especially when the logarithms of the coefficients in the observation equations are more readily obtained than the values themselves.

The General Expressions for the Unknown Quantities.

128. In writing general expressions for the most probable values of the unknown quantities, and in deriving their probable errors, we shall, for simplicity in notation, suppose that the observation equations have been reduced to the weight unity as explained in Art. 126, so that they are represented by equations (1), and the normal equations by equations (2) of Art. 124.

Let D be the symmetrical determinant of the coefficients of the unknown quantities in the normal equations, thus

$$D = \begin{vmatrix} \Sigma a^2 & \Sigma ab & \ldots & \Sigma al \\ \Sigma ab & \Sigma b^2 & \ldots & \Sigma bl \\ \cdot & \cdot & & \cdot \\ \cdot & \cdot & & \cdot \\ \cdot & \cdot & & \cdot \\ \Sigma al & \Sigma bl & \ldots & \Sigma l^2 \end{vmatrix} ;$$

let D_x denote the result of replacing the first column by a column consisting of the second members, Σan, Σbn, ... Σln; and let D_y, D_z, ... D_t be the like results for the remaining columns. Then

$$x = \frac{D_x}{D}, \quad y = \frac{D_y}{D}, \quad \ldots \quad t = \frac{D_t}{D} \quad . \quad (1)$$

are the general expressions for the unknown quantities.

129. Let the value of x when expanded in terms of the second members of the normal equations be

$$x = Q_1 \Sigma an + Q_2 \Sigma bn + \ldots + Q_\mu \Sigma ln. \quad . \quad . \quad (2)$$

Now, in the expansion of the determinant D_x in terms of the elements of its first column, the coefficients of Σan, Σbn, ... Σln are the first minors corresponding to Σa^2, Σab, ... Σal, in the determinant D.

Denoting the first of these by D_1, so that

$$D_1 = \begin{vmatrix} \Sigma b^2 & \Sigma bc & \ldots & \Sigma bl \\ \Sigma bc & \Sigma c^2 & \ldots & \Sigma cl \\ \cdot & \cdot & & \cdot \\ \cdot & \cdot & & \cdot \\ \cdot & \cdot & & \cdot \\ \Sigma bl & \Sigma cl & \ldots & \Sigma l^2 \end{vmatrix},$$

it follows, on comparing the values of x in equations (1) and (2), that

$$Q_1 = \frac{D_1}{D}.$$

In like manner, the values of Q_2, Q_3, ... Q_μ are the results of dividing the other first minors by D.

The Weights of the Unknown Quantities.

130. Let the value of x, when fully expanded in terms of the second members n_1, n_2, ... n_m of the observation equations, be

$$x = a_1 n_1 + a_2 n_2 + \ldots + a_m n_m. \quad . \quad . \quad . \quad (3)$$

Then, if r_x denotes the probable error of x, and r that of a standard observation, that is, the common probable error of each of the observed values n_1, n_2, ... n_m, we shall have, by Art. 89,

$$r_x^2 = r^2 . \Sigma a^2.$$

The precision with which x has been determined is usually expressed by means of its weight, that of a standard observation being taken as unity. The weights being inversely proportional to the squares of the probable errors, we have, therefore, for that of x,

$$p_x = \frac{1}{\Sigma a^2}.$$

131. Since the value of x is obtained from the normal equations, we do not actually find the values of the a's; we therefore proceed to express Σa^2 in terms of the quantities which occur in the normal equations.

Equating the coefficients of $n_1, n_2, \ldots n_m$ in equations (2) and (3), we find

$$\left. \begin{aligned}
a_1 &= a_1 Q_1 + b_1 Q_2 + \ldots + l_1 Q_\mu \\
a_2 &= a_2 Q_1 + b_2 Q_2 + \ldots + l_2 Q_\mu \\
&\;\cdot \quad \cdot \quad \cdot \quad \cdot \quad \cdot \quad \cdot \quad \cdot \\
a_m &= a_m Q_1 + b_m Q_2 + \ldots + l_m Q_\mu
\end{aligned} \right\} \quad \ldots \quad \textbf{(1)}$$

Multiplying the first of these equations by a_1, the second by a_2, and so on, and adding the results, we have

$$\Sigma a^2 = \Sigma aa \cdot Q_1 + \Sigma ba \cdot Q_2 + \ldots + \Sigma la \cdot Q_\mu. \quad (2)$$

The value of Σaa is found by multiplying the first of equations (1) by a_1, the second by a_2, and so on, and adding. The result is

$$\Sigma aa = \Sigma a^2 \cdot Q_1 + \Sigma ab \cdot Q_2 + \ldots + \Sigma al \cdot Q_\mu. \quad (3)$$

Multiplying this equation by D, the second member becomes the expansion of the determinant D in terms of the elements of its first column. Hence

$$\Sigma aa = 1. \quad \ldots \quad \ldots \quad \ldots \quad (4)$$

In like manner we find

$$\Sigma ba = \Sigma ab \cdot Q_1 + \Sigma b^2 \cdot Q_2 + \ldots + \Sigma bl \cdot Q_\mu, \quad (5)$$

and when this equation is multiplied by D, the second member is the expansion of a determinant in which the first two columns are identical. Thus $\Sigma ba = 0$, and in the same way we can show that $\Sigma ca, \ldots \Sigma la$ vanish.*

Substituting in equation (2), we have now

$$\Sigma a^2 = Q_1; \quad \ldots \ldots \ldots \quad (6)$$

hence from Arts. 130 and 129 we have, for the general expression for the weight of x,

$$p_x = \frac{1}{Q_1} = \frac{D}{D_1}. \quad \ldots \ldots \quad (7)$$

132. It follows from equation (2), Art. 129, that if in solving the normal equations we retain the second members in algebraic form, putting for them $A, B, C, \ldots$, then *the weight of x will be the reciprocal of the coefficient of A in the value of x.*† In like manner, that of y will be the reciprocal of the coefficient of B in the value of y, and so on.

For example, if the normal equations given in Art. 123 are written in the form

$$\begin{aligned}
27x + 6y &= A, \\
6x + 15y + z &= B, \\
y + 54z &= C,
\end{aligned}$$

the solution is

$$\begin{aligned}
19899x &= 809A - 324B + 6C, \\
737y &= -12A + 54B - C, \\
6633z &= 2A - 9B + 123C.
\end{aligned}$$

---

*Comparing equation (3) with equation (2), Art. 129, we see that Σaa is the value which x would assume if in each normal equation the second member were equal to the coefficient of x. The system of equations so formed would evidently be satisfied by $x = 1, y = 0, z = 0, \ldots$ $t = 0$; hence $\Sigma aa = 1$. In like manner, comparing equation (5) with the same equation, we see that Σba is the value which x would assume if the second member of each normal equation were equal to the coefficient of y. This value would be zero; thus $\Sigma ba = 0$.

† If the value of the weight of x alone is required, it may be found as the reciprocal of what the value of x becomes when $A = 1, B = 0$, $C = 0, \ldots$, that is to say, when the second member of the first normal equation is replaced by unity, and that of each of the others by zero.

The weights of x, y and z are therefore

$$p_x = \frac{19899}{809} = 24.60,$$

$$p_y = \frac{737}{54} = 13.65,$$

$$p_z = \frac{6633}{123} = 53.93.$$

133. When the value of x is obtained by the method of substitution, the process may be so arranged that its weight shall be found at the same time. Let the other unknown quantities be eliminated successively by means of the other normal equations, the value of x being obtained from the first normal equation or normal equation for x. Then, if this equation has not been reduced by multiplication or division, the coefficient of A in the second member will still be unity, and the equation will be of the form

$$Rx = T + A,$$

where T depends upon the quantities B, C, ... Now it is shown in the preceding article that the weight of x is the reciprocal of the coefficient of A in the value of x; hence in the present form of the equation the weight is the coefficient of x.*

As an illustration, let us find the values of x and its weight in the example given above, the normal equation being

$$\begin{aligned}
27x + 6y \quad\quad &= 88, \\
6x + 15y + z &= 70, \\
y + 54z &= 107.
\end{aligned}$$

The last equation gives

$$z = -\frac{1}{54}y + \frac{107}{54},$$

---

* The effect of the substitution is always to diminish the coefficient of x; for, as mentioned in the foot-note to Art. 122, if the true values of y, z, ... t were known, the weight of x would be Σa^2, which is the original coefficient of x, and obviously the weight on this hypothesis would exceed p_x, which is the weight when y, z, ... t are also subject to error.

and if this is substituted in the second, we obtain

$$y = - \frac{324}{809} x + \frac{3673}{809}.$$

Finally, by the substitution of this value of y in the first normal equation, we obtain, before any reduction is made,

$$\frac{19899}{809} x = \frac{49154}{809};$$

whence

$$p_x = \frac{19899}{809}, \quad \text{and} \quad x = \frac{49154}{19899},$$

as before found.

The Determination of the Measure of Precision.

134. The most probable value of h in the case of observations of equal weight is that which gives the greatest possible value to P, Art. 120, that is, to the function

$$h^m e^{-h^2 (u_1^2 + u_2^2 + \ldots + u_m^2)},$$

in which the errors are denoted by $u_1, u_2, \ldots u_m$, so that we may retain $v_1, v_2, \ldots v_m$ to denote the residuals which correspond to the values of the unknown quantities derived from the normal equations. By differentiation we derive, as in Art. 69, for the determination of h,

$$\Sigma u^2 = \frac{m}{2h^2}. \quad \ldots \quad \ldots \quad (1)$$

The value of Σu^2 cannot, of course, be obtained, but it is known to exceed Σv^2, which is its minimum value, and the best value we can adopt is found by adding to Σv^2 the mean value of the excess, $\Sigma u^2 - \Sigma v^2$.

135. Let the true values of the unknown quantities be $x + \delta x, y + \delta y, \ldots t + \delta t$, while $x, y, \ldots t$ denote the values derived from the normal equations. We have then the residual equations

$$
\left.
\begin{aligned}
a_1x + b_1y + \ldots + l_1t - n_1 &= v_1 \\
a_2x + b_2y + \ldots + l_2t - n_2 &= v_2 \\
\cdots\cdots\cdots\cdots\cdots\cdots\cdots &\\
a_mx + b_my + \ldots + l_mt - n_m &= v_m
\end{aligned}
\right\} , \quad \ldots \quad (1)
$$

and, for the true errors, the expressions,

$$
\left.
\begin{aligned}
a_1(x + \delta x) + b_1(y + \delta y) + \ldots + l_1(t + \delta t) - n_1 &= u_1 \\
a_2(x + \delta x) + b_2(y + \delta y) + \ldots + l_2(t + \delta t) - n_2 &= u_2 \\
\cdots\cdots\cdots\cdots\cdots\cdots\cdots\cdots\cdots\cdots &\\
a_m(x + \delta x) + b_m(y + \delta y) + \ldots + l_m(t + \delta t) - n_m &= u_m
\end{aligned}
\right\} . (2)
$$

Multiplying equations (1) by $v_1, v_2, \ldots v_m$ respectively, and adding, the coefficient of x in the result is

$$
a_1v_1 + a_2v_2 + \ldots + a_mv_m,
$$

which vanishes by the first normal equation (1), Art. 121. In like manner, the coefficient of y vanishes by the second normal equation, and so on. Hence

$$
\Sigma v^2 = -\, \Sigma nv. \quad \ldots \quad \ldots \quad (3)
$$

Treating equations (2) in the same way, we have

$$
\Sigma uv = -\, \Sigma nv;
$$

hence

$$
\Sigma v^2 = \Sigma uv. \quad \ldots \quad \ldots \quad (4)
$$

Again, multiplying equations (1) by $u_1, u_2, \ldots u_m$, and adding,

$$
\Sigma uv = \Sigma au \cdot x + \Sigma bu \cdot y + \ldots + \Sigma lu \cdot t - \Sigma nu;
$$

and treating equations (2) in the same way,

$$
\Sigma u^2 = \Sigma au\,(x + \delta x) + \Sigma bu\,(y + \delta y) + \ldots + \Sigma lu\,(t + \delta t) - \Sigma nu.
$$

Subtracting the preceding equation, we have, by equation (4),

$$
\Sigma u^2 - \Sigma v^2 = \Sigma au \cdot \delta x + \Sigma bu \cdot \delta y + \ldots + \Sigma lu \cdot \delta t, \quad (5)
$$

an expression for the correction whose mean value we are seeking.

136. Expressions for $\delta x,\ \delta y,\ \ldots\ \delta t$ are readily obtained as follows. Treating equations (2) exactly as the residual equations (1) are treated to form the normal equations, we find

$$
\left.
\begin{aligned}
\Sigma a^2.(x+\delta x)+\Sigma ab.(y+\delta y)+\ldots \\
+\ \Sigma al.(t+\delta t)=\Sigma an+\Sigma au \\
\Sigma ab.(x+\delta x)+\Sigma b^2.(y+\delta y)+\ldots \\
+\ \Sigma bl.(t+\delta t)=\Sigma bn+\Sigma bu \\
\cdot\ \cdot\ \cdot\ \cdot\ \cdot\ \cdot\ \cdot\ \cdot\ \cdot\ \cdot\ \cdot\ \cdot\ \cdot\ \cdot \\
\Sigma al.(x+\delta x)+\Sigma bl.(y+\delta y)+\ldots \\
+\ \Sigma l^2.(t+\delta t)=\Sigma ln+\Sigma lu
\end{aligned}
\right\}.
$$

Subtraction of the corresponding normal equation from each of these gives the system,

$$
\left.
\begin{aligned}
\Sigma a^2.\delta x+\Sigma ab.\delta y+\ldots+\Sigma al.\delta t=\Sigma au \\
\Sigma ab.\delta x+\Sigma b^2.\delta y+\ldots+\Sigma bl.\delta t=\Sigma bu \\
\cdot\ \cdot\ \cdot\ \cdot\ \cdot\ \cdot\ \cdot\ \cdot\ \cdot\ \cdot\ \cdot\ \cdot\ \cdot \\
\Sigma al.\delta x+\Sigma bl.\delta y+\ldots+\Sigma l^2.\delta t=\Sigma lu
\end{aligned}
\right\},
$$

a comparison of which with the normal equations shows that $\delta x,\ \delta y,\ \ldots\ \delta t$ are the same functions of $u_1,\ u_2,\ \ldots\ u_m$ that $x, y, \ldots t$ are of $n_1,\ n_2,\ \ldots\ n_m$. Hence we have

$$
\delta x = a_1 u_1 + a_2 u_2 + \ldots + a_m u_m,
$$

where $a_1,\ a_2,\ \ldots\ a_n$ have the same meaning as in Art. 130.

137. Consider now the first term, $\Sigma au.\delta x$, of the value of $\Sigma u^2 - \Sigma v^2$, equation (5), Art. 135. Multiplying the value of δx just found by

$$
\Sigma au = a_1 u_1 + a_2 u_2 + \ldots + a_m u_m,
$$

the product consists of terms containing squares and products of the errors. We are concerned only with the mean values of these terms, in accordance with the law of facility, which is for each error $\dfrac{h}{\sqrt{\pi}}\,e^{-h^2 u^2}$. Since the mean value of each error is zero, it is obvious that the mean value of each product vanishes;

so that the mean value of $\Sigma au \cdot \delta x$ is the mean value of

$$a_1 a_1 u_1^2 + a_2 a_2 u_2^2 + \ldots + a_m a_m u_m^2.$$

Now by Art. 50 the mean value of each of the squares $u_1^2, u_2^2, \ldots u_m^2$ is $\dfrac{1}{2h^2}$; hence the mean value of $\Sigma au \cdot \delta x$ is $\dfrac{\Sigma aa}{2h^2}$, or, by equation (4), Art. 131, $\dfrac{1}{2h^2}$.

In the same manner it can be shown that the mean value of each term in the second member of equation (5), Art. 135, is $\dfrac{1}{2h^2}$; hence that of $\Sigma u^2 - \Sigma v^2$ is $\dfrac{\mu}{2h^2}$, and the best value we can adopt for Σu^2 is

$$\Sigma u^2 = \Sigma v^2 + \frac{\mu}{2h^2}.$$

Substituting this in equation (1), Art. 134, we have

$$\Sigma v^2 = \frac{m - \mu}{2h^2}, \quad \text{whence} \quad h = \sqrt{\frac{m - \mu}{2 \Sigma v^2}}.$$

The Probable Errors of the Observations and Unknown Quantities.

138. The resulting values of the mean and probable error of a single observation are

$$\varepsilon = \frac{1}{h \sqrt 2} = \sqrt{\frac{\Sigma v^2}{m - \mu}}, \quad \ldots \quad \ldots \quad (1)$$

$$r = \frac{\rho}{h} = \rho \sqrt 2 \sqrt{\frac{\Sigma v^2}{m - \mu}} = 0.6745 \sqrt{\frac{\Sigma v^2}{m - \mu}}; \quad (2)$$

and the probable errors of the unknown quantities are

$$r_x = \frac{r}{\sqrt{p_x}}, \quad r_y = \frac{r}{\sqrt{p_y}}, \quad \ldots \quad r_t = \frac{r}{\sqrt{p_t}}. \quad (3)$$

When the observation equations have not equal weights we

may replace Σv^2, which represents the sum of the squares of the residuals in the reduced equations, by $\Sigma p v^2$, in which the residuals are derived from the original observation equations. The formulæ (1) and (2) will then give the mean and probable errors of an observation whose weight is unity.

It will be noticed that when $\mu = 1$ the formulæ reduce to those given in Art. 72 for the case of one unknown quantity.

139. Instead of calculating the values of $v_1, v_2, \ldots v_m$ directly from the residual equations, and squaring and adding the results, we may employ the formula for Σv^2 deduced below.

By equation (3), Art. 135,

$$\Sigma v^2 = -\ \Sigma n v.$$

Now multiplying equations (1) of that article by $n_1, n_2, \ldots n_m$ respectively, and adding the results, we have

$$\Sigma n v = \Sigma a n . x + \Sigma b n . y + \ldots + \Sigma l n . t - \Sigma n^2.$$

Therefore

$$\Sigma v^2 = \Sigma n^2 - \Sigma a n . x - \Sigma b n . y - \ldots - \Sigma l n . t. \quad . \quad (1)$$

The quantity Σn^2 which occurs in this formula may be calculated at the same time with the coefficients in the normal equations. It enters with them into the check equations of Art. 127.

We may also express Σv^2 exclusively in terms of these quantities, for if we write

$$D_n = \begin{vmatrix} \Sigma a^2 & \Sigma ab & \ldots & \Sigma al & \Sigma an \\ \Sigma ab & \Sigma b^2 & \ldots & \Sigma bl & \Sigma bn \\ \cdot & \cdot & & \cdot & \cdot \\ \cdot & \cdot & & \cdot & \cdot \\ \cdot & \cdot & & \cdot & \cdot \\ \Sigma al & \Sigma bl & \ldots & \Sigma l^2 & \Sigma ln \\ \Sigma an & \Sigma bn & \ldots & \Sigma ln & \Sigma n^2 \end{vmatrix},$$

and consider the development of D_n in terms of the elements of its last row, we see that

$$D_n = -\ \Sigma a n . D_x - \Sigma b n . D_y - \ldots - \Sigma l n . D_t + \Sigma n^2 . D,$$

where $D, D_x, \ldots D_t$ have the same meanings as in Art. 128; hence

$$\Sigma v^2 = \frac{D_n}{D}. \quad \cdots \quad \cdot \quad (2)$$

140. For example, in the case of the four observation equations of Art. 115,

$$\left.\begin{array}{r} x - y + 2z = 3 \\ 3x + 2y - 5z = 5 \\ 4x + y + 4z = 21 \\ -x + 3y + 3z = 14 \end{array}\right\},$$

for which the normal equations are solved in Art. 123, the value of Σn^2 is 671; and formula (1) gives

$$\Sigma v^2 = 671 - 88 \times \frac{49154}{19899} - 70 \times \frac{70659}{19899}$$

$$- 107 \times \frac{38121}{19899} = \frac{1600}{19899},$$

in which 1600 is the value of D_n. Substituting this value of Σv^2 in the formulæ of Art. 138, we find

$$\varepsilon = 0.2836, \qquad r = 0.1913$$

for the mean and probable errors of an observation; and using the weights found in Art. 132, we find for those of the unknown quantities

$$\begin{array}{lll} \varepsilon_x = 0.057, & \varepsilon_y = 0.077, & \varepsilon_z = 0.039, \\ r_x = 0.038, & r_y = 0.052, & r_z = 0.026. \end{array}$$

In this example we have found the exact value of Σv^2; if approximate computations are employed, the formula used has the disadvantage that a very small quantity is to be found by means of large positive and negative terms, which considerably increases the number of significant figures to which the work must be carried. Thus, because $\Sigma n^2 = 671$ in the above example, the work would have to be carried out with seven-place logarithms to obtain Σv^2 to four decimal places. The direct computation of the v^2's from the observation equations would present the same difficulty in a less degree.

141. Of course, no great confidence can be placed in the absolute values of the probable errors obtained from so small a number of observation equations as in the example given above. There being but one more observation than barely sufficient to determine values of the unknown quantities, the case is comparable to that in which $n = 2$ when the observations are direct.

By increasing the number of observations we not only obtain a more trustworthy determination of the probable error of a single observation, but, what is more important, we increase the weight, and hence the precision, of the unknown quantities. The measure in which this takes place depends greatly upon the character of the equations with respect to independence. As already mentioned in Art. 113, if there were only μ equations it would be necessary that they should be independent; in other words, the determinant of their coefficients must not vanish, otherwise the values of the unknown quantities will be indeterminate. When this state of things is approached the values are ill-determined, and this is indicated by the small value of the determinant in question. The same thing is true of the normal equations. Accordingly, the weights are small when the determinant D is small; thus the value of D is in a general way a measure of the efficiency of the system of observation equations in determining the unknown quantities.

142. If we write the coefficients in the m observation equations in a rectangular form, thus,

$$
\begin{array}{cccccc}
a_1 & a_2 & \cdots & a_\mu & \cdots & a_m \\
b_1 & b_2 & \cdots & b_\mu & \cdots & b_m \\
\cdot & \cdot & & \cdot & & \cdot \\
\cdot & \cdot & & \cdot & & \cdot \\
\cdot & \cdot & & \cdot & & \cdot \\
l_1 & l_2 & \cdots & l_\mu & \cdots & l_m
\end{array}
$$

the determinant D is, by a theorem in determinants, the sum of the squares of all the determinants which can be formed by selecting μ columns of the rectangular array. The first of these determinants is that of the coefficients of the first μ equations, which, as we have seen, vanishes when they are not independent, and the others are the like determinants for all the other combinations of μ equations which can be formed from the m observation equations. It follows that D cannot be negative, and cannot vanish unless there is no set of μ independent equations among the observation equations.

143. By a similar consideration of the values of D_x, D_y, ... D_t, Art. 128, it has been shown * that, for each unknown quantity, the value given by the normal equations is the weighted mean of all the values which could be derived from μ selected equations, the weights being the squares of the corresponding determinants.†

Empirical or Interpolation Formulæ.

144. A set of observation equations usually arises in the following manner: One of two varying quantities is a function of another, *of known form,* the constants which occur having, however, unknown values. Simultaneous values of the varying quantities are observed. The values of the second quantity (the independent variable in the functional expression) are regarded as accurate, and from them are computed in each case the values of the coefficients when the other variable is treated as a linear function of the unknown quantities. This other variable is then the observed quantity M of our observation equations, and the errors are the differences between the observed values and those which accurately correspond to the assumed values of the independent variable.

---

* J. W. L. Glaisher, *Monthly Notices of the Royal Ast. Soc.,* vol. xl, 1880, p. 607 et seq.

† When there is but a single unknown quantity, say x, its coefficients $a_1, a_2, \ldots$ take the place of these determinants, and the weight of the result is accordingly Σa^2. Compare Art. 122. In general, as between two unknown quantities, the weight of that which has the greater coefficients will be the greater.

Taking the two variable quantities as coordinates, the observations may be represented by points, and the problem before us is that of determining a curve of known variety in such a manner as to pass as nearly as possible through these points.

145. But it may happen that, while we know that a functional relation between the variable quantities exists, we have no theoretic knowledge of the form of the function. In such cases, our only resource is to assume the form of the function, being guided therein by an inspection of the points representing the observations. An equation so assumed is sometimes called *an empirical formula*. The constants involved in it are determined exactly as in the case of formulæ having a theoretical basis. The final result can only be judged of by the residuals. If these are numerous enough, their failure to follow the law of accidental errors may indicate the inadequacy of the assumed form.

When the formula as determined is used to compute the probable values of the observed quantity corresponding to other values of the independent variable, it is called *an interpolation formula*. The results can never be satisfactory except for values within the range of the values corresponding to the observations upon which the formula is based.

Conditioned Observations.

146. We have hitherto supposed the unknown quantities to be independent of one another, so that any set of simultaneous values is possible, and before the observations all sets are regarded as equally probable. It frequently happens, however, that the unknown quantities are required to satisfy rigorously certain *equations of condition*, in addition to the observation equations which must be approximately satisfied. The μ unknown quantities may thus be subject to ν equations of condition, where $\nu < \mu$, while the whole number of equations $m + \nu$ exceeds μ. The case may be reduced to that already discussed by the elimination of μ' unknown quantities from the observation equations by means of the equations of condition, leaving us with m

observation equations containing $\mu - \nu$ independent unknown quantities.

We shall consider only the case (which is of frequent occurrence) in which $m = \mu$, and the observation equations express direct determinations of the μ unknown quantities.

147. Let $M_1, M_2, \ldots M_\mu$ be the observed values of $X, Y, \ldots T$, with weights $p_1, p_2, \ldots p_\mu$, and put

$$X = M_1 + x, \quad Y = M_2 + y, \quad \ldots \quad T = M_\mu + t,$$

so that $x, y, \ldots t$ are the required corrections to the observed values. The equations of condition may be reduced as in Art. 117 to the linear forms

$$\left. \begin{array}{l} a_1 x + a_2 y + \ldots + a_\mu t = E_1 \\ b_1 x + b_2 y + \ldots + b_\mu t = E_2 \\ \cdot \;\; \cdot \;\; \cdot \;\; \cdot \;\; \cdot \;\; \cdot \;\; \cdot \;\; \cdot \;\; \cdot \\ f_1 x + f_2 y + \ldots + f_\mu t = E_\nu \end{array} \right\} \quad \ldots \ldots \; (1)$$

The values of $x, y, \ldots t$ must satisfy these equations, which are, however, insufficient in number to determine them, and, by the principle of Least Squares, those values are most probable which, while satisfying equations (1), make

$$p_1 x^2 + p_2 y^2 + \ldots + p_\mu t^2 = \text{a minimum.}$$

In other words, the values must be such that

$$p_1 x\,dx + p_2 y\,dy + \ldots + p_\mu t\,dt = 0, \quad \ldots \; (2)$$

for all possible simultaneous values of $dx, dy, \ldots dt$, that is, for all values which satisfy the equations,

$$\left. \begin{array}{l} a_1 dx + a_2 dy + \ldots + a_\mu dt = 0 \\ b_1 dx + b_2 dy + \ldots + b_\mu dt = 0 \\ \cdot \;\; \cdot \;\; \cdot \;\; \cdot \;\; \cdot \;\; \cdot \;\; \cdot \;\; \cdot \;\; \cdot \\ f_1 dx + f_2 dy + \ldots + f_\mu dt = 0 \end{array} \right\}, \quad \ldots \; (3)$$

derived by differentiating equations (1). Hence, denoting the first member of equation (2) by P and those of equations (3) by $S_1, S_2, \ldots S_\nu$, the conditions are fulfilled by values which satisfy equations (1) and make

$$P - k_1 S_1 - k_2 S_2 - \ldots - k_\nu S_\nu = 0, \quad \ldots \quad (4)$$

where $k_1, k_2, \ldots k_\nu$ are any constants.

This last equation will be satisfied if we can equate to zero the coefficient of each of the differentials, thus putting

$$\left.\begin{aligned}
p_1 x &= k_1 a_1 + k_2 b_1 + \ldots + k_\nu f_1 \\
p_2 y &= k_1 a_2 + k_2 b_2 + \ldots + k_\nu f_2 \\
&\cdot \quad \cdot \quad \cdot \quad \cdot \quad \cdot \quad \cdot \quad \cdot \quad \cdot \quad \cdot \\
p_\mu t &= k_1 a_\mu + k_2 b_\mu + \ldots + k_\nu f_\mu
\end{aligned}\right\}, \quad \ldots \quad (5)$$

and this it is possible to do because we have μ unknown quantities and ν auxiliary quantities $k_1, k_2, \ldots k_\nu$ which can be determined so as to satisfy the $\nu + \mu$ equations comprised in the groups (1) and (5).

148. Substituting the values of $x, y, \ldots t$ from equations (5) in equations (1), we have a set of linear equations to determine the k's which are called the *correlatives* of the equations of condition. These equations may be written in the form

$$\left.\begin{aligned}
k_1 \Sigma \frac{a^2}{p} + k_2 \Sigma \frac{ab}{p} + \ldots + k_\nu \Sigma \frac{af}{p} &= E_1 \\
k_1 \Sigma \frac{ab}{p} + k_2 \Sigma \frac{b^2}{p} + \ldots + k_\nu \Sigma \frac{bf}{p} &= E_2 \\
\cdot \quad \cdot \quad \cdot \quad \cdot \quad \cdot \quad \cdot \quad \cdot \quad \cdot \quad \cdot \quad \cdot \quad \cdot \\
k_1 \Sigma \frac{af}{p} + k_2 \Sigma \frac{bf}{p} + \ldots + k_\nu \Sigma \frac{f^2}{p} &= E_\nu
\end{aligned}\right\}, \quad \cdot \quad (6)$$

in which the summation refers to the coefficients of the several unknown quantities; thus, for example, $\Sigma \dfrac{a^2}{p}$ is the sum of the squares of all the coefficients in the first equation of condition each divided by the weight of the corresponding unknown quantity. The correlatives being found from these equations, the values of the corrections $x, y, \ldots t$ are given at once by equations (5).

149. When there is but one equation of condition

$$a_1 x + a_2 y + \ldots + a_\mu t = E,$$

the second members of equations (5) reduce to their first terms, and the equations require that the corrections of the several unknown quantities shall be proportional to their coefficients in the equation of condition divided by their weights. Equations (6) then reduce to the single equation

$$k \Sigma \frac{a^2}{p} = E,$$

and the corrections are

$$x = \frac{\dfrac{a_1}{p_1}}{\Sigma \dfrac{a^2}{p}} E, \qquad y = \frac{\dfrac{a_2}{p_2}}{\Sigma \dfrac{a^2}{p}} E, \qquad \ldots$$

In the very common case in which the numerical value of each coefficient in the single equation of condition is unity (for example, when the successive angles at a point, or all the angles of a polygon, are measured, or when the sum of two measured angles is independently measured), we have the simple rule that *the corrections are inversely proportional to the weights.*

Examples.

1. Denoting the heights above mean sea level of five points by X, Y, Z, U, V, observations of difference of level gave, in feet:

$$
\begin{array}{lll}
X = 573.08 & Z - Y = 167.33 & U - V = 425.00 \\
Y - X = 2.60 & U - Z = 3.80 & V = 319.91 \\
Y = 575.27 & U - Y = 170.28 & V = 319.75
\end{array}
$$

Putting $X = 573 + x$, $Y = 575 + y$, $Z = 742 + z$, $U = 745 + u$,

$V = 320 + v$, find the values and probable errors of the corrections x, y, z, u, v, supposing the observations to have equal weight.

$$x = -0.19 \pm 0.23, \quad y = 0.14 \pm 0.21, \quad z = 0.05 \pm 0.30,$$
$$u = 0.43 \pm 0.25, \quad v = 0.03 \pm 0.19.$$

2. Given the observation equations:

$$x = 4.5, \qquad y = 1.6, \qquad x - y = 2.7,$$

with weights 10, 5 and 3 respectively, determine the values of x and y. $\qquad x = 4.468 \pm 0.049, \quad y = 1.663 \pm 0.063.$

3. Measurements of the ordinates of a straight line corresponding to the abscissas 4, 6, 8 and 9, gave the values 5, 8, 10 and 12. What is the most probable equation of the line in the form $y = mx + b$? $\qquad y = 1.339x - 0.029.$

4. Given the observation equations of equal weight:

$$x = 10, \qquad y - x = 7, \qquad y = 18,$$
$$y - z = 9, \qquad x - z = 2,$$

determine the most probable values of the unknown quantities, and the probable errors of an observation and of each unknown quantity. $\qquad x = 10\tfrac{3}{8}, \quad y = 17\tfrac{5}{8}, \quad z = 8\tfrac{1}{4},$
$$r = r_z = 0.29, \quad r_x = r_y = 0.23.$$

5. In order to determine the length x at $0°$ C. of a meter bar, and its expansion y for each degree of temperature, it was measured at temperatures $20°, 40°, 50°, 60°$, the corresponding observed lengths being 1000.22, 1000.65, 1000.90 and 1001.05 mm. respectively. Find the probable values of x and y with their probable errors. $\qquad x = 999^{mm}.804 \pm 0.033,$
$$y = 0^{mm}.0212 \pm 0.0007.$$

6. The length of the pendulum which beats seconds is known to vary with the latitude in accordance with Clairant's equation,

$$l = l' + \left(\frac{5}{2} q - \mu \right) l' \sin^2 L,$$

where l' is the length at the equator, q the ratio $\frac{1}{289}$ of the centrifugal force at the equator to the weight, and μ the compression of the meridian regarded as unknown.   Putting

$$l' = 991^{mm} + x, \qquad \left(\frac{5}{2}\, q - \mu\right) l' = y,$$

observations in different latitudes gave in millimeters :

$$x + 0.969y = 5.13, \qquad x + 0.095y = 0.56, \qquad x + 0.327y = 1.70,$$
$$x + 0.749y = 3.97, \qquad x \qquad\quad = 0.19, \qquad x + 0.685y = 3.62,$$
$$x + 0.426y = 2.24, \qquad x + 0.152y = 0.77, \qquad x + 0.793y = 4.23.$$

Find the length at the equator with its probable error.

$$l' = 991^{mm}.069 \pm .026.$$

7. Find the value of μ in the preceding example and its probable error. $\mu = \frac{1}{294} \pm 0.00046.$

8. The measured height in feet of A above O, B above A and B above O are 12.3, 14.1 and 27.0 respectively.   Find the most probable value and the probable error of each of these differences of level. 12.5 ± 0.17; 14.3 ± 0.17; 26.8 ± 0.17.

9. A round of angles at a station in the U. S. Coast Survey was observed with weights as follows :

$65°\ 11'\ 52''.500$ with weight 3, $87°\ 2'\ 24''.703$ with weight 3,
$66\ \ 24\ \ 15\ .553$ "   "   3, $141\ 21\ \ 21\ .757$ "   "   1;
find the adjusted values whose sum must be $360°$.

$$65°\ 11'\ 53''.4145, \quad 87°\ 2'\ 25''.6175,$$
$$66\ \ 24\ \ 16\ .4675, \quad 141\ 21\ \ 24\ .5005.$$

10. Four observations on the angle X of a triangle gave a mean of $36°\ 25'\ 47''$, two observations on Y gave a mean of $90°\ 36'\ 28''$ and three on Z gave $52°\ 57'\ 57''$.   Find the adjusted values of the angles and the probable error of a single observation. $r = 7''.7$; $X = 36°\ 25'\ 44''.23$,
$$Y = 90\ \ 36\ \ 22\ .46,$$
$$Z = 52\ \ 57\ \ 53\ .31.$$

11. A round of four angles was observed as follows :

$38°\ 52'\ 14''.28$ weight 2, $44°\ 35'\ 56''.54$ weight 3,
$145\ \ 23\ \ 16\ .35$ "   4, $131\ 10\ \ 21\ .47$ "   3;
find the adjusted values.

$$38°\ 51'\ 35''.94, \quad 44°\ 35'\ 30''.98,$$
$$145\ \ 22\ \ 57\ .18, \quad 131\ \ 9\ \ 55\ .91.$$

12. Measurements of the angles between surrounding stations were made with weights as follows:

Between stations 1 and 2,   55° 57′ 58″.68, weight 3,
"   "   2 " 3,   48 49 13 .64,   "   19,
"   "   1 " 3, 104 47 12 .66,   "   17,
"   "   3 " 4,   54 38 15 .53,   "   13,
"   "   2 " 4, 103 27 28 .99,   "   6.

Find the corrections of the angles in the order given.

0″.285, 0″.005, − 0″.050, − 0″.058, 0″.127.

IX.

GAUSS'S METHOD OF SUBSTITUTION.

The Reduced Normal Equations.

150. In solving the normal equations, it becomes essential, except in the simplest cases, to reduce the labor as much as possible by adopting a systematic process in the elimination. We shall here give the method of substitution as developed by Gauss, which has the advantage of preserving, in each of the sets of simultaneous equations which arise in the elimination, the symmetry which exists in the coefficients of the normal equations, thereby materially diminishing the number of coefficients to be calculated.

The m observation equations, involving the μ unknown quantities $x, y, z, \ldots t$, being, as in Art. 124,

$$\left. \begin{array}{l} a_1 x + b_1 y + \ldots + l_1 t = n_1 \\ a_2 x + b_2 y + \ldots + l_2 t = n_2 \\ \cdot \quad \cdot \quad \cdot \quad \cdot \quad \cdot \quad \cdot \\ a_m x + b_m y + \ldots + l_m t = n_m \end{array} \right\}, \quad \ldots \ (1)$$

let the normal equations be written in the form

$$\left. \begin{array}{l} [aa]x + [ab]y + [ac]z + \ldots + [al]t = [an] \\ [ab]x + [bb]y + [bc]z + \ldots + [bl]t = [bn] \\ [ac]x + [bc]y + [cc]z + \ldots + [cl]t = [cn] \\ \cdot \quad \cdot \quad \cdot \quad \cdot \quad \cdot \quad \cdot \quad \cdot \\ [al]x + [bl]y + [cl]z + \ldots + [ll]t = [ln] \end{array} \right\} \ . \ . \ (2)$$

As mentioned at the end of Art. 126, we may suppose the observation equations (1) to have been reduced to the weight unity, so that $[aa], [ab], \ldots [ln]$ stand for $\Sigma a^2, \Sigma ab, \ldots \Sigma ln$.

151. The value of x in terms of the other unknown quantities derived from the first of equations (2), or normal equation for x, is

$$x = -\frac{[ab]}{[aa]}y - \frac{[ac]}{[aa]}z - \ldots + \frac{[an]}{[aa]}.$$

Substituting this in the $\mu - 1$ other equations, they become

$$\left.\begin{array}{l}
\left([bb] - [ab]\dfrac{[ab]}{[aa]}\right)y + \left([bc] - [ab]\dfrac{[ac]}{[aa]}\right)z + \ldots = [bn] - [ab]\dfrac{[an]}{[aa]} \\[2ex]
\left([bc] - [ac]\dfrac{[ab]}{[aa]}\right)y + \left([cc] - [ac]\dfrac{[ac]}{[aa]}\right)z + \ldots = [cn] - [ac]\dfrac{[an]}{[aa]} \\[2ex]
\quad \cdot \quad \cdot \quad \cdot \quad \cdot \quad \cdot \quad \cdot \quad \cdot \quad \cdot \\[1ex]
\left([bl] - [al]\dfrac{[ab]}{[aa]}\right)y + \ldots + \left([ll] - [al]\dfrac{[al]}{[aa]}\right)t = [ln] - [al]\dfrac{[an]}{[aa]}
\end{array}\right\},$$

in which it will be noticed that the coefficients of the unknown quantities have the same symmetry as in the normal equations (2). These equations for the $\mu - 1$ unknown quantities $y, z, \ldots t$ are called *the reduced normal equations*, and are written in the form

$$\left.\begin{array}{l}
[bb, 1]y + [bc, 1]z + \ldots + [bl, 1]t = [bn, 1] \\
[bc, 1]y + [cc, 1]z + \ldots + [cl, 1]t = [cn, 1] \\
\quad \cdot \quad \cdot \quad \cdot \quad \cdot \quad \cdot \quad \cdot \\
[bl, 1]y + [cl, 1]z + \ldots + [ll, 1]t = [ln, 1]
\end{array}\right\}, \quad \cdot \ (3)$$

in which

$$\left.\begin{array}{l}
[bb, 1] = [bb] - \dfrac{[ab][ab]}{[aa]} \\[2ex]
[bc, 1] = [bc] - \dfrac{[ab][ac]}{[aa]} \\[1ex]
\quad \cdot \quad \cdot \quad \cdot \quad \cdot \\[1ex]
[ln, 1] = [ln] - \dfrac{[al][an]}{[aa]}
\end{array}\right\} \cdot \ \ldots \ldots (4)$$

Equations (4) show that the rule for the formation of the coefficients and the second members of the reduced normal equations is the same throughout; namely, from the corresponding coefficient in the normal equations we are to subtract the result of multiplying together the two expressions in whose symbols one of the letters in the given symbol is associated with *a*, and dividing the product by $[aa]$.

The Elimination Equations.

152. Eliminating y by means of the first of the reduced normal equations (3) from each of the others, just as x was eliminated from the normal equations, and employing a similar notation, we have the $\mu - 2$ equations

$$\left.\begin{aligned} [cc, 2]z + \ldots + [cl, 2]t &= [cn, 2] \\ \cdot \quad \cdot \quad \cdot \quad \cdot \quad \cdot \quad \cdot \quad \cdot \\ [cl, 2]z + \ldots + [ll, 2]t &= [ln, 2] \end{aligned}\right\}, \quad \ldots \ (5)$$

which may be called the *second reduced normal equations.* The coefficients in these equations are derived from those in equations (3) exactly as the latter were found from those in equations (2). Thus

$$\left.\begin{aligned} [cc, 2] &= [cc, 1] - \frac{[bc, 1][bc, 1]}{[bb, 1]} \\ \cdot \quad \cdot \quad \cdot \quad \cdot \quad \cdot \quad \cdot \\ [ln, 2] &= [ln, 1] - \frac{[bl, 1][bn, 1]}{[bb, 1]} \end{aligned}\right\} \quad \cdot \ \cdot \ \cdot \ \cdot \ (6)$$

In like manner the third reduced normal equations are formed from these last, the coefficients being distinguished by the postfixed numeral 3, corresponding to the number of variables which have been eliminated. We finally arrive at the single equation

$$[ll, \mu - 1]t = [ln, \mu - 1], \quad \cdots \quad \cdot (7)$$

which determines the unknown quantity standing last in the order of elimination.

153. The quantity which immediately precedes t is next derived from the first of the preceding set of equations (that is, from the equation by means of which it was eliminated) by the substitution of the numerical value found for t; and so on, until finally x is found from the first of the original normal equations. The equations from which the unknown quantities are actually determined are therefore the following :

$$\left.\begin{array}{l}[aa]x + [ab]y + [ac]z + \ldots + [al]t = [an] \\ [bb, 1]y + [bc, 1]z + \ldots + [bl, 1]t = [bn, 1] \\ [cc, 2]z + \ldots + [cl, 2]t = [cn, 2] \\ \qquad \cdot \quad \cdot \quad \cdot \quad \cdot \quad \cdot \quad \cdot \\ \qquad\qquad [ll, \mu - 1]t = [ln, \mu - 1]\end{array}\right\} \cdot (8)$$

These are called the *final* or *elimination equations*.

The Reduced Observation Equations.

154. Let us suppose that there exists a relation between the variables which must be exactly satisfied, while the m observation equations are to be satisfied approximately. Let this relation be

$$\alpha x + \beta y + \ldots + \lambda t = \nu. \quad \cdots \quad (1)$$

Eliminating x from the observation equations (1), Art. 150 by the substitution of

$$x = -\frac{\beta}{\alpha}y - \frac{\gamma}{\alpha}z - \ldots - \frac{\lambda}{\alpha}t + \frac{\nu}{\alpha},$$

derived from this equation, we have

$$\left.\begin{aligned}
\left(b_1 - a_1\frac{\beta}{\alpha}\right)y + \left(c_1 - a_1\frac{\gamma}{\alpha}\right)z + \ldots + \left(l_1 - a_1\frac{\lambda}{\alpha}\right)t = n_1 - a_1\frac{\nu}{\alpha} \\
\left(b_2 - a_2\frac{\beta}{\alpha}\right)y + \left(c_2 - a_2\frac{\gamma}{\alpha}\right)z + \ldots + \left(l_2 - a_2\frac{\lambda}{\alpha}\right)t = n_2 - a_2\frac{\nu}{\alpha} \\
\cdot \quad \cdot \quad \cdot \quad \cdot \quad \cdot \quad \cdot \quad \cdot \quad \cdot \quad \cdot \\
\left(b_m - a_m\frac{\beta}{\alpha}\right)y + \left(c_m - a_m\frac{\gamma}{\alpha}\right)z + \ldots + \left(l_m - a_m\frac{\lambda}{\alpha}\right)t = n_m - a_m\frac{\nu}{\alpha}
\end{aligned}\right\},$$

which may be called *the reduced observation equations*, and written in the form

$$\left.\begin{aligned}
b_1'y + c_1'z + \ldots + l_1't = n_1' \\
b_2'y + c_2'z + \ldots + l_2't = n_2' \\
\cdot \quad \cdot \quad \cdot \quad \cdot \quad \cdot \\
b_m'y + c_m'z + \ldots + l_m't = n_m'
\end{aligned}\right\}, \quad \ldots \quad (2)$$

a comparison of which with the equations written above sufficiently indicates the values of $b_1', c_1', \ldots a_m', \ldots n_m'$.

The $\mu - 1$ normal equations derived from these are

$$\left.\begin{aligned}
[b'b']y + [b'c']z + \ldots + [b'l']t = [b'n'] \\
[b'c']y + [c'c']z + \ldots + [c'l']t = [c'n'] \\
\cdot \quad \cdot \quad \cdot \quad \cdot \quad \cdot \quad \cdot \quad \cdot \\
[b'l']y + [c'l']z + \ldots + [l'l']t = [l'n']
\end{aligned}\right\}, \quad \cdot \quad (3)$$

in which

$$\left.\begin{aligned}
[b'b'] &= \Sigma\left(b - a\frac{\beta}{\alpha}\right)^2 = [bb] - 2[ab]\frac{\beta}{\alpha} + [aa]\frac{\beta^2}{\alpha^2} \\
[b'c'] &= \Sigma\left(b - a\frac{\beta}{\alpha}\right)\left(c - a\frac{\gamma}{\alpha}\right) = [bc] - [ab]\frac{\gamma}{\alpha} - [ac]\frac{\beta}{\alpha} + [aa]\frac{\beta\gamma}{\alpha^2} \\
\cdot \quad \cdot \quad \cdot \quad \cdot \quad \cdot \quad \cdot \quad \cdot \quad \cdot \quad \cdot \\
[l'n'] &= \Sigma\left(l - a\frac{\lambda}{\alpha}\right)\left(n - a\frac{\nu}{\alpha}\right) = [ln] - [al]\frac{\nu}{\alpha} - [an]\frac{\lambda}{\alpha} + [aa]\frac{\lambda\nu}{\alpha^2}
\end{aligned}\right\}. (4)$$

155. Let us now suppose that the equation of condition (1) which is to be exactly satisfied is identical with the first of the normal equations (2) of Art 150, so that

$$\alpha = [aa], \quad \beta = [ab], \quad \ldots \quad \nu = [an];$$

then equations (4) become

$$\left.\begin{aligned}
[b'b'] &= [bb] - \frac{[ab]^2}{[aa]} \\[2mm]
[b'c'] &= [bc] - \frac{[ab][ac]}{[aa]} \\[2mm]
&\quad \cdot \quad \cdot \quad \cdot \quad \cdot \\[2mm]
[l'n'] &= [ln] - \frac{[al][an]}{[aa]}
\end{aligned}\right\} \quad \cdots \cdots \quad (5)$$

Comparison of these with equations (4), Art. 151, shows that the normal equations (3) of the preceding article now become identical with the first reduced normal equations of Art. 151. Hence *the first reduced normal equations are the same as the normal equations corresponding to the reduced observation equations which would result if x were eliminated from the observation equations by means of the normal equation for x.*

It is evident that, in like manner, the second reduced normal equations are the same as the $\mu - 2$ normal equation which would result from the reduced observation equations, if they were further reduced by the elimination of y by means of the reduced normal equation for y; or, what is the same thing, the normal equations which would result if x and y were eliminated from the original observation equations by means of the normal equations for x and y. Similar remarks apply to the other sets of reduced normal equations.

156. An important consequence of what has just been proved is that, among the coefficients in the reduced normal equations, or *auxiliary quantities*, those of quadratic form,

$$[bb, 1], \quad [cc, 1], \quad \ldots \quad [cc, 2], \quad \ldots \quad [ll, \mu - 1],$$

being, like the corresponding quantities in the normal equations, sums of squares, are all positive. It is further to be noticed that each of these quantities decreases as its postfix increases, for the subtractive quantities in the formation of the successive values are themselves positive. For example,

$$[ll, 1] = [ll] - \frac{[al]^2}{[aa]}, \quad [ll, 2] = [ll, 1] - \frac{[bl, 1]^2}{[bb, 1]}.$$

Weights of the Two Quantities First Determined.

157. The unknown quantity t has been determined in equation (7), Art. 152, after the manner described in Art. 133; that is to say, from its own normal equation—no reduction by multiplication or division having taken place in the course of the elimination. Hence, as proved in that article, its weight is the coefficient of the unknown quantity; that is to say, the weight of an observation being unity, that of t is

$$p_t = [ll, \mu - 1],$$

which, as shown in the preceding article, is necessarily a positive quantity.*

The weight of any one of the unknown quantities might be determined, in like manner, by making it the last in the order of elimination.

158. Let s be the unknown quantity preceding t, so that

$$[ll, \mu - 1] = [ll, \mu - 2] - \frac{[kl, \mu - 2]^2}{[kk, \mu - 2]},$$

---

* As shown in Art. 156, the substitutions diminish the successive coefficients of t. Compare the foot-note to Art. 133, p. 104. In fact $[ll]$ is the weight that t would have if the true values of all the other quantities were known; $[ll, 1]$ is the weight which it would have if all the others except x were known—that is, if x and t were the only quantities subject to error; and so on.

or

$$[ll, \mu - 1][kk, \mu - 2] = [ll, \mu - 2][kk, \mu - 2] - [kl, \mu - 2]^2.$$

If now the order of s and t be reversed, no other change of order being made, the auxiliaries with the postfix $\mu - 2$ will be unaltered, and we shall have

$$[kk, \mu - 1][ll, \mu - 2] = [kk, \mu - 2][ll, \mu - 2] - [kl, \mu - 2]^2,$$

hence

$$[kk, \mu - 1][ll, \mu - 2] = [ll, \mu - 1][kk, \mu - 2].$$

But $[kk, \mu - 1]$ is the weight of s, therefore we have

$$p_s = [kk, \mu - 1] = \frac{[kk, \mu - 2]}{[ll, \mu - 2]}[ll, \mu - 1].$$

The weights of the other unknown quantities cannot be thus readily expressed in terms of the auxiliaries occurring in the calculation of t. A general method of obtaining all the weights will be given in Arts. 174–176.

The Reduced Expression for Σv^2.

159. We have found in Art. 139 for Σv^2 or $[vv]$ the expression

$$[vv] = -[an]x - [bn]y - \ldots - [ln]t + [nn],$$

which is similar in form to the expressions equated to zero in the normal equations. If in this we substitute the value of x, as in Art. 151, it becomes

$$[vv] = -[bn, 1]y - [cn, 1]z - \ldots - [ln, 1]t + [nn, 1],$$

in which

$$[bn, 1] = [bn] - \frac{[ab][an]}{[aa]},$$

. . . . .

$$[nn, 1] = [nn] - \frac{[an][an]}{[aa]},$$

after the analogy of the auxiliary quantities defined in equations (4), Art. 151. In like manner, by the elimination of y, $[vv]$ is reduced to the form

$$[vv] = -[cn, 2]z - \ldots - [ln, 2]t + [nn, 2],$$

and finally, by the substitution of the value of t, to

$$[vv] = [nn, \mu],$$

the postfix μ indicating that all the unknown quantities have been eliminated.

Substituting in the expressions for the mean and probable error of an observation, Art. 138, we have

$$\epsilon = \sqrt{\frac{[nn, \mu]}{m - \mu}}, \qquad r = 0.6745 \sqrt{\frac{[nn, \mu]}{m - \mu}}.$$

The General Expression for the Sum of the Squares of the Errors.

160. The following articles contain an investigation* of the sum of the squares of the errors considered as a function of the unknown quantities, showing directly that the minimum

---

* Gauss, "Theoria Motus Corporum Cœlestium," Art. 182; *Werke*, vol. vii. p. 238.

value of this quantity corresponds to the values derived from the normal equations, and is equal to $[nn, \mu]$, and also deriving from the general expression the law of facility of error in t, and thence its weight.

Let

$$W = [vv] \quad . \quad . \quad . \quad . \quad . \quad . \quad (1)$$

be the sum of the squares of the errors in the observation equations, that is to say, of the linear expressions of the form (Art. 119),

$$ax + by + \ldots + lt - n = v.$$

The absolute term in W is obviously $[nn]$. Put

$$\frac{1}{2}\frac{dW}{dx} = X, \quad \frac{1}{2}\frac{dW}{dy} = Y, \quad \ldots \quad \frac{1}{2}\frac{dW}{dt} = T. \quad . \quad (2)$$

Then

$$X = \Sigma v \frac{dv}{dx} = [av] = [aa]x + [ab]y + \ldots + [al]t - [an]. \quad (3)$$

The equations $X = 0,\ Y = 0, \ldots T = 0$ are the normal equations.   Now, since

$$\frac{1}{2}\frac{d(X^2)}{dx} = X\frac{dX}{dx} = [aa]X, \quad \text{or,} \quad \frac{1}{2}\frac{d}{dx}\frac{X^2}{[aa]} = X,$$

$$\frac{1}{2}\frac{d}{dx}\left(W - \frac{X^2}{[aa]}\right) = 0;$$

hence, if we put

$$W_1 = W - \frac{X^2}{[aa]}, \quad . \quad . \quad . \quad . \quad . \quad (4)$$

W_1 is a function independent of x. Now, in equation (4), W_1 has for all values of the variables which make $X = 0$

the same value as W; hence W_1 is what W becomes when x is eliminated from it by means of the first normal equation, $X = 0$.

161. It follows from what has just been proved, that

$$W_1 = [v'v'] \; ; \quad \cdots \quad (5)$$

that is to say, W_1 is the sum of the squares of expressions of the form

$$b'y + c'z + \ldots + l't - n' = v',$$

corresponding to the reduced observation equations, Arts. 154, 155. The absolute term in W_1 is therefore $[n'n']$ or $[nn, 1]$.

If, now, we put

$$Y_1 = \frac{1}{2}\frac{dW_1}{dy}, \quad \ldots \quad T_1 = \frac{1}{2}\frac{dW_1}{dt}, \quad \cdots \quad (6)$$

$$Y_1 = \Sigma v'\frac{dv'}{dy} = [b'v'] = [b'b']y + [b'c']z + \ldots + [b'l']t - [b'n']. \, (7)$$

and $Y_1 = 0, \ldots T_1 = 0$, are the reduced normal equations.

The relation between the expressions $Y_1, \ldots T_1$ and $X, Y, \ldots T$ is derived from equation (4); thus, differentiating with respect to Y,

$$Y_1 = Y - \frac{X}{[aa]}\frac{dX}{dy} = Y - \frac{[ab]}{[aa]}X, \cdots \quad (8)$$

which gives another proof of the identity of the coefficients $[b'b'], \ldots [b'n']$ with $[bb, 1], \ldots [bn, 1]$, established in Art. 155. We now prove, exactly as in the preceding article, that

$$W_2 = W_1 - \frac{Y_1^2}{[bb, 1]} \quad \cdots \quad (9)$$

is a function independent of y as well as of x, and is identical with $[v''v'']$, the sum of the squares of expressions of the form

$$c''z + \ldots + l''t - n'' = v''$$

corresponding to the second reduced observation equations, from which x and y have been eliminated by means of the equations $X = 0$, $Y_1 = 0$. The absolute term in W_2 is obviously $[n''n'']$ or $[nn, 2]$.

162. Proceeding in this way, we finally arrive at an expression W_μ which is independent of all the variables, and consists simply of the absolute term $[nn, \mu]$. We have thus reduced W to the form

$$W = \frac{X^2}{[aa]} + \frac{Y_1^2}{[bb, 1]} + \frac{Z_2^2}{[cc, 2]} + \ldots + \frac{T_{\mu-1}^2}{[ll, \mu-1]} + [nn, \mu].^* \quad (10)$$

The denominators $[aa]$, $[bb, 1]$, $\ldots$ $[ll, \mu-1]$, being sums of squares, are all positive; hence the minimum value of W is the value $[nn, \mu]$ corresponding to the values of $x, y, \ldots t$ which satisfy the equations $X = 0$, $Y_1 = 0$, $\ldots$ $T_{\mu-1} = 0$.

163. Since W is the sum of the squares of the errors, the probability that the actual observations should occur is proportional to e^{-h^2W} as in Art. 62. Therefore, by the principle explained in Art. 30, the observations having been made, the probabilities of different systems of values of the unknown quantities are proportional to the corresponding values of this function. Hence, C being a constant to be determined, the elementary probability, Art. 21, of a given system of values of $x, y, \ldots t$ is

$$Ce^{-h^2W} dx\, dy \ldots dt, \quad \ldots \ldots \quad (11)$$

---

* This result is also derived by Gauss in a purely algebraic manner in the "Disquisitio de Elementis Ellipticis Paladis;" *Werke*, vol. vi. p. 22. See also Encke, *Berliner Astronomisches Jahrbuch* for 1853, pp. 273–277.

where h is the measure of precision of an observation, and C is such that the integral of the expression for all possible values of the variables is unity.

The probability of a given system of values of $y, z, \ldots t$, while x may have any value, is found by summing this expression for all values of x. It is then

$$C \, dy \ldots dt \int_{-\infty}^{\infty} e^{-h^2 W} dx = C dy \ldots dt \, e^{-h^2 W_1} \int_{-\infty}^{\infty} e^{-h^2 \frac{X^2}{[aa]}} dx,$$

since W_1 in equation (4) is independent of x. Since $\dfrac{dX}{dx} = [aa]$, the value of the definite integral in this expression is, by equation (7), Art. 39,

$$\int_{-\infty}^{\infty} e^{-h^2 \frac{X^2}{[aa]}} dx = \frac{1}{[aa]} \int_{-\infty}^{\infty} e^{-\frac{h^2}{[aa]} X^2} dX = \frac{\sqrt{\pi}}{h \sqrt{[aa]}}.$$

Thus the probability of a given system of values of y, $z, \ldots t$ is

$$\frac{C \sqrt{\pi}}{h \sqrt{[aa]}} dy dz \ldots dt \, e^{-h^2 W_1} \ldots \ldots \quad (12)$$

164. In like manner, the probability of a given system of values of $z \ldots t$, x and y being indeterminate, is

$$\frac{C \sqrt{\pi}}{h \sqrt{[aa]}} dz \ldots dt \int_{-\infty}^{\infty} e^{-h^2 W_1} dy,$$

which, by equations (9) and (7), reduces to

$$\frac{C \sqrt{(\pi^2)}}{h^2 \sqrt{\{[aa][bb, 1]\}}} dz \ldots dt \, e^{-h^2 W_2}. \quad \ldots \quad (13)$$

Proceeding in this way, we have, finally, for the prcbability of a given value of t,

$$\frac{C\sqrt{(\pi^{\mu-1})}dt}{h^{\mu-1}\sqrt{\{[aa][bb,1]\ldots[kk,\mu-2]\}}}e^{-h^2W_{\mu-1}}\ .\ .\ (14)$$

Again, integrating this for all values of t, we have

$$C\frac{\sqrt{(\pi^\mu)}e^{-h^2[nn,\mu]}}{h^\mu\sqrt{\{[aa][bb,1]\ldots[ll,\mu-1]\}}}=1\ .\ .\ .\ (15)$$

Substituting the value of C thus determined, we obtain for the probability of t,

$$\frac{h\sqrt{[ll,\mu-1]}}{\sqrt{\pi}}e^{-h^2(W_{\mu-1}-[nn,\mu])}dt.\ .\ .\ .\ (16)$$

But

$$W_{\mu-1}=\frac{T^2_{\mu-1}}{[ll,\mu-1]}+[nn,\mu]$$

and

$$T_{\mu-1}=[ll,\mu-1]t-[ln,\mu-1];$$

therefore, putting

$$\tau=\frac{T_{\mu-1}}{[ll,\mu-1]}=t-\frac{[ln,\mu-1]}{[ll,\mu-1]},$$

and omitting dt, the expression (16) gives for the law of facility of error in t,

$$\frac{h\sqrt{[ll,\mu-1]}}{\sqrt{\pi}}e^{-h^2[ll,\mu-1]\tau^2}.\ .\ .\ .\ .\ (17)$$

This is of the same form as the law of facility for **an** observation, except that the measure of precision is

$$h \sqrt{[ll, \mu - 1]}.$$

Thus the most probable value of t is that which makes $\tau = 0$, namely,

$$t = \frac{[ln, \mu - 1]}{[ll, \mu - 1]},$$

and the weight of this determination, when that of an observed quantity is unity, is

$$p_t = [ll, \mu - 1].$$

The Auxiliaries Expressed in Determinant Form.

165. If, in the determinant of the coefficients of the normal equations, denoted by D in Art. 128, we subtract from the second row the product of the first row multiplied by $\dfrac{[ab]}{[aa]}$, it becomes

$$0, \quad [bb, 1], \quad [bc, 1], \quad \ldots \quad [bl, 1].$$

Treating the other rows in like manner, the determinant D is reduced to a form in which the first row is unchanged, and the rest are replaced by a column of 0's and the determinant of the first reduced normal equations. Denoting this last determinant by D', we have $D = [aa]D'$.

By a similar reduction of D', D is further reduced to a form in which the first two rows are as in that described above, and the rest are replaced by two columns of 0's and the determinant, D'', of the second reduced normal equations. Finally, D is thus reduced to the determinant of the elimination equations (8), Art. 153.

The successive forms of D give the equations

$$D=[aa]D'=[aa][bb,1]D''=\ldots=[aa][bb,1][cc,2]\ldots[ll,\mu-1].$$

166. If, in the form of D involving $D^{(r)}$, we take the first r rows, and then any other row (which will therefore be a row belonging to $D^{(r)}$), the same reasoning shows that any determinant formed by selecting $r+1$ columns of this rectangular block is equal to the minor occupying the same position in D.

We can now express any auxiliary, say $[\alpha\beta, r]$, as the quotient of two minors, of the $(r+1)$th and rth degree respectively, in D. This auxiliary occurs in the form of D just mentioned. Taking the first r rows and columns together with the row and column in which the given auxiliary occurs, we have a determinant whose value is

$$[aa][bb,1]\ldots[\gamma\gamma,r-1][\alpha\beta,r],$$

because all the elements below the principal diagonal vanish. But this determinant is equal to that similarly situated in D, and the coefficient of $[\alpha\beta, r]$ is equal to the determinant formed from the first r rows and columns of D. For example, for $[de, 2]$ we have

$$\begin{vmatrix} [aa] & [ab] & [ae] \\ 0 & [bb,1] & [be,1] \\ 0 & 0 & [de,2] \end{vmatrix} = \begin{vmatrix} [aa] & [ab] & [ae] \\ [ab] & [bb] & [be] \\ [ad] & [bd] & [de] \end{vmatrix},$$

and

$$\begin{vmatrix} [aa] & [ab] \\ 0 & [bb,1] \end{vmatrix} = \begin{vmatrix} [aa] & [ab] \\ [ab] & [bb] \end{vmatrix};$$

therefore

$$[de,2]\begin{vmatrix} [aa] & [ab] \\ [ab] & [bb] \end{vmatrix} = \begin{vmatrix} [aa] & [ab] & [ae] \\ [ab] & [bb] & [be] \\ [ad] & [bd] & [de] \end{vmatrix}.$$

167. The same principle holds if we include the auxiliaries involving the letter n, and in particular the determinant D_n of Art. 139 is

$$D_n = [aa][bb, 1] \ldots [ll, \mu - 1][nn, \mu] = D[nn, \mu];$$

therefore

$$[nn, \mu] = \frac{D_n}{D},$$

which is the same value that was found for $[vv]$ on p. 110.

Form of the Calculation of the Auxiliaries.

168. In calculating the coefficients which occur in the elimination equations and the value of $[vv]$, it is important to arrange the work in tabular form, and to apply frequent checks to the computation to secure accuracy. In the annexed table,* which is constructed for four unknown quantities, the first compartment contains the coefficients and second members of the normal equations together with the value of $[nn]$, which are derived from the observation equations, as explained in Art. 127. The coefficients are entered opposite and below the letters in their symbols, those below the diagonal line, whose values are the same as those symmetrically situated above, being omitted. Beneath those in the first line are written their logarithms, which are used in computing the subtractive quantities placed beneath each of the other coefficients.

---

* The tabular arrangement is taken from W. Jordan's "Handbuch der Vermessungskunde." See also Oppolzer's "Lehrbuch zur Bahnbestimmung der Kometen und Planeten," vol. ii. p. 340 *et seq.*, where the table, with a somewhat different arrangement, is given for six unknown quantities, and an example is fully worked out.

	a	b	c	d	n	s
a	$[aa]$ $\log [aa]$	$[ab]$ $\log [ab]$	$[ac]$ $\log [ac]$	$[ad]$ $\log [ad]$	$[an]$ $\log [an]$	$[as]$ $\log [as]$
b	$\log A_b$	$[bb]$ $A_b[ab]$	$[bc]$ $A_b[ac]$	$[bd]$ $A_b[ad]$	$[bn]$ $A_b[an]$	$[bs]$ $A_b[as]$
c	$\log A_c$		$[cc]$ $A_c[ac]$	$[cd]$ $A_c[ad]$	$[cn]$ $A_c[an]$	$[cs]$ $A_c[as]$
d	$\log A_d$			$[dd]$ $A_d[ad]$	$[dn]$ $A_d[an]$	$[ds]$ $A_d[as]$
n	$\log A_n$				$[nn]$ $A_n[an]$	$[ns]$ $A_n[as]$
b		$[bb,1]$ $\log [bb,1]$	$[bc,1]$ $\log [bc,1]$	$[bd,1]$ $\log [bd,1]$	$[bn,1]$ $\log [bn,1]$	$[bs,1]$ $\log [bs,1]$
c	$\log B_c$		$[cc,1]$ $B_c[bc,1]$	$[cd,1]$ $B_c[bd,1]$	$[cn,1]$ $B_c[bn,1]$	$[cs,1]$ $B_c[bs,1]$
d	$\log B_d$			$[dd,1]$ $B_d[bd,1]$	$[dn,1]$ $B_d[bn,1]$	$[ds,1]$ $B_d[bs,1]$
n	$\log B_n$				$[nn,1]$ $B_n[bn,1]$	$[ns,1]$ $B_n[bs,1]$
c			$[cc,2]$ $\log [cc,2]$	$[cd,2]$ $\log [cd,2]$	$[cn,2]$ $\log [cn,2]$	$[cs,2]$ $\log [cs,2]$
d	$\log C_d$			$[dd,2]$ $C_d[cd,2]$	$[dn,2]$ $C_d[cn,2]$	$[ds,2]$ $C_[cs,2]$
n	$\log C_n$				$[nn,2]$ $C_n[cn,2]$	$[ns,2]$ $C_n[cs,2]$
d				$[dd,3]$ $\log [dd,3]$	$[dn,3]$ $\log [dn,3]$	$[ds,3]$ $\log [ds,3]$
n	$\log D_n = \log t$				$[nn,3]$ $D_n[dn,3]$	$[ns,3]$ $D_n[ds,3]$
n	$t =$		$[vv] =$		$[nn,4]$	$[ns,4]$

In expressing the subtractive quantities we have adopted for abridgment the notation

$$A_b = \frac{[ab]}{[aa]}, \quad A_c = \frac{[ac]}{[aa]}, \quad A_d = \frac{[ad]}{[aa]}, \quad A_n = \frac{[an]}{[aa]}.$$

The logarithms of these quantities are placed at the side, and, adding them successively to the logarithms above, the antilogarithms of the sums are entered in their places. After this is done, the results of subtraction are the auxiliaries with postfix 1, which are to be placed in corresponding positions in the compartment below.

In like manner the third compartment is formed from the second, and in expressing the subtractive quantities we have put

$$B_c = \frac{[bc, 1]}{[bb, 1]}, \quad B_d = \frac{[bd, 1]}{[bb, 1]}, \quad B_n = \frac{[bn, 1]}{[bb, 1]}.$$

So also we have put

$$C_d = \frac{[cd, 2]}{[cc, 2]}, \quad C_n = \frac{[cn, 2]}{[cc, 2]};$$

and finally,

$$D_n = \frac{[dn, 3]}{[dd, 3]},$$

which is also the value of t. Thus the first four compartments correspond to the several sets of normal equations, and their first lines to the four elimination equations. Finally, in the fifth compartment we have computed $[nn, 4]$, which is the value of $[vv]$.

Check Equations.

169. The column headed s is added for the sake of the check equations

$$\left. \begin{aligned} [aa] + [ab] + [ac] + [ad] + [an] + [as] &= 0 \\ [ab] + [bb] + [bc] + [bd] + [bn] + [bs] &= 0 \\ \cdots \cdots \cdots \cdots \cdots \cdots \cdots \cdots \cdots \\ [an] + [bn] + [cn] + [dn] + [nn] + [ns] &= 0 \end{aligned} \right\}, \quad . \quad (1)$$

the quantities $[as], \ldots [ns]$ being formed as in Art. 127, except that we have changed the sign of s, so that for each observation equation

$$a + b + c + d + n + s = 0.$$

The checks are applied before the logarithms and subtractive quantities are entered. They require that the algebraic sum of the quantities in each line together with those standing above the first term should vanish.

Similar checks can be applied in each of the lower compartments. For example, if from the second of equations (1) we subtract the product of the first equation multiplied by A_b, we have, since $A_b[aa] = [ab]$,

$$0 + [bb, 1] + [bc, 1] + [bd, 1] + [bn, 1] + [bs, 1] = 0,$$

where $[bs, 1]$ has been formed in precisely the same way as the other auxiliaries, namely,

$$[bs, 1] = [bs] - \frac{[ab][as]}{[aa]}.$$

In the same manner we obtain the other equations of the group

$$\left. \begin{array}{l} [bb, 1] + [bc, 1] + [bd, 1] + [bn, 1] + [bs, 1] = 0 \\ \cdot \quad \cdot \quad \cdot \quad \cdot \quad \cdot \quad \cdot \quad \cdot \quad \cdot \quad \cdot \quad \cdot \quad \cdot \quad \cdot \quad \cdot \quad \cdot \quad \cdot \quad \cdot \\ [bn, 1] + [cn, 1] + [dn, 1] + [nn, 1] + [ns, 1] = 0 \end{array} \right\} \quad (2)$$

So also we have similar checks involving the auxiliaries which have the postfix 2, and those which have the postfix 3, and finally

$$[nn, 4] + [ns, 4] = 0.$$

	a	b	c	d	n	s	
a	3.1217	.5756	− .1565	− .0067	1.5710	−5.1050	1
	0.49439	9.76012	9_n19451	7_n82607	0.19618	0_n70800	
b		2.9375	.1103	− .0015	− .9275	−2.6943	1
A_b	9.26573	.1061	− .0289	− .0012	.2897	− .9413	
c			4.1273	.2051	− .0652	−4.2211	−1
A_c	8_n70012		.0078	.0003	− .0788	.2559	
d				4.1328	− .0178	−4.3118	1
A_d	7_n33168			.0000	− .0034	.0110	
n					1.3409	−1.9016	−2
A_n	9.70179				.7906	−2.5692	
b		2.8314	.1392	− .0003	−1.2172	−1.7530	1
		0.45200	9.14364	6_n47712	0_n08536	0_n24378	
c			4.1195	.2048	.0136	−4.4770	1
B_c	8.69164		.0068	.0000	− .0598	− .0862	
d				4.1328	− .0144	−4.3228	1
B_d	6_n02512			.0000	.0001	.0002	
n					.5503	.6676	−1
B_n	9_n63336				.5233	.7536	
c			4.1127	.2048	.0734	−4.3908	1
			0.61413	9.31133	8.86570	0_n64254	
d				4.1328	− .0145	−4.3230	1
C_d	8.69720			.0102	.0037	− .2186	
n					.0270	− .0860	−1
C_n	8.25157				.0013	− .0784	
d				4.1226	− .0182	−4.1044	0
				0.61517	8_n26007	0_n61325	
n					.0257	− .0076	−1
D_n	$7_n64490 = \log t$				.0001	.0181	
n	$t = - .004415$	$[vv] = .02565$			.0256	− .0257	−1

Numerical Example.

170. As an illustration, let us take the following normal equations :

$$3.1217x + .5756y - .1565z - .0067t = 1.5710$$
$$.5756x + 2.9375y + .1103z - .0015t = -.9275$$
$$-.1565x + .1103y + 4.1273z + .2051t = -.0652$$
$$-.0067x - .0015y + .2051z + 4.1328t = -.0178$$

together with

$$[nn] = 1.3409,$$

which were derived from sixteen observation equations, while at the same time the values of $[as], \ldots [ns]$ were found as in the first compartment of the table. The numbers in the final column are the sums which should equal zero according to the check equations, the small errors being due to the rejection of decimals beyond the fourth place. The letters at the side and top indicate the symbol for each auxiliary, while the compartment gives the postfix. Since there are two computations for $[vv]$, namely $[nn, 4]$ and $- [ns, 4]$, which agree within the limits of the uncertainty of logarithmic computation, we take for its value a mean between them. Putting $m = 16$ and $\mu = 4$ in the formulæ for ϵ and r, this value gives

$$\epsilon = .04623, \qquad r = .03118,$$

for the mean and probable error of an observation.

Values of the Unknown Quantities from the Elimination Equations.

171. Dividing the elimination equations, (8), Art. 153, by $[aa], [bb, 1], [cc, 2], [dd, 3]$, and using the notation introduced in Art. 168, they become

$$x + A_b y + A_c z + A_d t = A_n$$
$$y + B_c z + B_d t = B_n$$
$$z + C_d t = C_n$$
$$t = D_n$$

　　. . . (1,

The following table gives the form in which the computation is conveniently arranged, and its application to the example for which the elimination equations are found in Art. 170.

D_n $-C_d t$	C_n $-C_d t$	B_n $-B_d t$ $-B_c z$	A_n $-A_d t$ $-A_c z$ $-A_b y$
t $\log t$	z $\log z$	y $\log y$	x
$-.004415$	$.017847$ $.000220$	$-.42989$ $.00000$ $-.00089$	$.50325$ $-.00001$ $.00091$ $.07943$
$-.004415$ $7_n 64490$	$.018067$ 8.25689	$-.43078$ $9_n 63426$	$.58358$

The weight of t is, by Art. 157, $[dd, 3]$, and that of z is, by Art. 158, $\dfrac{[cc, 2]}{[dd, 2]}[dd, 3]$; employing the values computed in Art. 170, we have

$$\log p_t = 0.61517, \qquad \log p_z = 0.61305,$$
$$p_t = 4.1226, \qquad p_z = 4.1025 ;$$

and dividing the values of ϵ and t found above by the square roots of the weights, we have for t,

$$\epsilon_t = .02277, \qquad r_t = .01536;$$

and for z,

$$\epsilon_z = .02282, \qquad r_z = .01539.$$

Values of the Unknown Quantities Found Independently.

172. In order to obtain the general expressions for the weights, it is necessary first to express the values of the unknown quantities independently of each other. For this purpose we multiply equations (1) of the preceding article by 1, α_1, α_2, α_3, respectively, and add the results, assuming the α's to be so determined that the coefficients of y, z, and t vanish. We shall thus have

$$x = A_n + B_n\alpha_1 + C_n\alpha_2 + D_n\alpha_3, \quad \cdots \quad (2)$$

and, for the determination of the α's,

$$\left. \begin{array}{l} A_b + \alpha_1 \qquad\qquad\qquad = 0 \\ A_c + B_c\alpha_1 + \alpha_2 \qquad\quad = 0 \\ A_d + B_d\alpha_1 + C_d\alpha_2 + \alpha_3 = 0 \end{array} \right\} \quad \cdots \quad (3)$$

In like manner, to find y we multiply the second, third and fourth of equations (1) by 1, β_2, β_3, respectively, and add. The result is

$$y = B_n + C_n\beta_2 + D_n\beta_3, \quad \cdots \cdots \quad (4)$$

where the β's are determined by

$$\left. \begin{array}{l} B_c + \beta_2 \qquad\quad = 0 \\ B_d + C_d\beta_2 + \beta_3 = 0 \end{array} \right\} \quad \cdots \cdots \quad (5)$$

Again, multiplying the last two of equations (1) by 1, γ_3, and adding

$$z = C_n + D_n\gamma_3, \quad \cdots \cdots \quad (6)$$

where γ_3 is determined by

$$C_d + \gamma_3 = 0. \quad \cdots \cdots \quad (7)$$

173. The form for the computation of α_1, α_2, α_3, β_2, β_3, γ_3, according to equations (3), (5), and (7), and the numerical work for the example of Art. 170, is as follows:

$-A_b$	$-A_c$ $-B_c\alpha_1$	$-A_d$ $-B_d\alpha_1$ $-C_d\alpha_2$
α_1 $\log \alpha_1$	α_2 $\log \alpha_2$	α_3 $\log \alpha_3$
	.050133 .009065	.002146 −.000020 −.002948
9_n26573	.059198 8.77231	−.000822 6_n91487

$-B_c$	$-B_d$ $-C_d\beta_2$
β_2 $\log \beta_2$	β_3 $\log \beta_3$
	.000106 .002448
8_n69164	.002554 7.40722

$$-C_d = \gamma_3$$
$$\log \gamma_3 = 8_n69720$$

The values of α_1, β_2 and γ_3 are not found, as their logarithms only are needed.

We may now recompute the values of the unknown quantities by means of equations (2), (4), (6) by way of verifying the values of $\alpha_1, \ldots \gamma_3$ as well as those of $x, \ldots t$. The form of computation will be as below:

A_n $B_n\alpha_1$ $C_n\alpha_2$ $D_n\alpha_3$	B_n $C_n\beta_2$ $D_n\beta_3$	C_n $D_n\gamma_3$	D_n
x	y	z	t
.50325	−.42989	.017847	−.004415
.07927	−.00088	.000220	
.00106	−.00001		
.00000			
.58358	−.43078	.018067	−.004415

The numerical values agree exactly with those found in Art. 171.

The Weights of the Unknown Quantities.

174. The principle by which we obtain expressions for the weights is that proved in Art. 132, namely: When the value of any one of the unknown quantities is expressed in terms of the second members of the normal equations, its weight is the reciprocal of the coefficient of the second member of its own normal equation; or what is the same thing: *The reciprocal of the weight is what the value of the unknown quantity becomes when the second member of its own normal equation is replaced by unity and that of each of the others by zero.*

Restoring the values of the quantities A_n, B_n, C_n, D_n, the values of x, y, z, t, Art. 172, are

$$\left.\begin{aligned}
x &= \frac{[an]}{[aa]} + \frac{[bn, 1]}{[bb, 1]}\alpha_1 + \frac{[cn, 2]}{[cc, 2]}\alpha_2 + \frac{[dn, 3]}{[dd, 3]}\alpha_3 \\
y &= \frac{[bn, 1]}{[bb, 1]} + \frac{[cn, 2]}{[cc, 2]}\beta_2 + \frac{[dn, 3]}{[dd, 3]}\beta_3 \\
z &= \frac{[cn, 2]}{[cc, 2]} + \frac{[dn, 3]}{[dd, 3]}\gamma_3 \\
t &= \frac{[dn, 3]}{[dd, 3]}
\end{aligned}\right\} \quad (1)$$

Equations (3), (5), and (7), Art. 172, show that the values of $\alpha_1, \ldots \gamma_3$ are independent of the values of $[an]$, $[bn]$, $[cn]$, and $[dn]$; hence the changes indicated above, in order to convert the second members of equations (1) into the expressions for the reciprocals of the weights, have only to be made in the numerators $[an]$, $[bn, 1]$, $[cn, 2]$, and $[dn, 3]$, where, by the definitions given in Arts. 151 and 152, we have, using the notation of Art. 168,

$$\left.\begin{aligned}
[bn, 1] &= [bn] - A_b[an] \\
[cn, 2] &= [cn] - A_c[an] - B_c[bn, 1] \\
[dn, 3] &= [dn] - A_d[an] - B_d[bn, 1] - C_d[cn, 2]
\end{aligned}\right\}. \quad (2)$$

175. To find the value of $\dfrac{1}{p_x}$, we must now put in the value of x

$$[an] = 1, \qquad [bn] = 0, \qquad [cn] = 0, \qquad [dn] = 0.$$

Making these substitutions and using equations (3), Art. 172, the value of $[bn, 1]$ becomes

$$[bn, 1] = - A_b = \alpha_1 ;$$

that of $[cn, 2]$ then becomes

$$[cn, 2] = - A_c - B_c\alpha_1 = \alpha_2 ;$$

and that of $[dn, 3]$ becomes

$$[dn, 3] = - A_d - B_d\alpha_1 - C_d\alpha_2 = \alpha_3 .$$

Hence from the first of equations (1) we infer

$$\frac{1}{p_x} = \frac{1}{[aa]} + \frac{\alpha_1^{\,2}}{[bb, 1]} + \frac{\alpha_2^{\,2}}{[cc, 2]} + \frac{\alpha_3^{\,2}}{[dd, 3]}.$$

176. Again, to obtain the weight of y, we put in the second of equations (1)

$$[an] = 0, \qquad [bn] = 1, \qquad [cn] = 0, \qquad [dn] = 0.$$

These substitutions in equations (2) give, with the aid of equations (5), Art. 172,

$$[bn,\ 1] = 1,$$
$$[cn,\ 2] = -B_c = \beta_2,$$
$$[dn,\ 3] = -B_d - C_d\beta_2 = \beta_3;$$

hence we have

$$\frac{1}{p_u} = \frac{1}{[bb,\ 1]} + \frac{\beta_2^{\ 2}}{[cc,\ 2]} + \frac{\beta_3^{\ 2}}{[dd,\ 3]}.$$

In like manner we complete the system of equations

$$\left.\begin{aligned}
\frac{1}{p_x} &= \frac{1}{[aa]} + \frac{\alpha_1^{\ 2}}{[bb,\ 1]} + \frac{\alpha_2^{\ 2}}{[cc,\ 2]} + \frac{\alpha_3^{\ 2}}{[dd,\ 3]} \\[4pt]
\frac{1}{p_y} &= \qquad\qquad \frac{1}{[bb,\ 1]} + \frac{\beta_2^{\ 2}}{[cc,\ 2]} + \frac{\beta_3^{\ 2}}{[dd,\ 3]} \\[4pt]
\frac{1}{p_z} &= \qquad\qquad\qquad\qquad \frac{1}{[cc,\ 2]} + \frac{\gamma_3^{\ 2}}{[dd,\ 3]} \\[4pt]
\frac{1}{p_t} &= \qquad\qquad\qquad\qquad\qquad\qquad \frac{1}{[dd,\ 3]}
\end{aligned}\right\}\ .\ \ .\ \ (3)$$

which are readily extended to the case of any number of unknown quantities.

177. The form of computation and its application to our numerical example are given on page 148, the values of the logarithms entered at the top and side being taken from the computations on pages 140 and 144.

From the logarithms in the last line and log $\epsilon^2 = 7.32990$, ($\epsilon^2 = \frac{1}{12}[vv]$, p. 140) we find for the mean errors

$$\epsilon_x = .02669, \quad \epsilon_y = .02750, \quad \epsilon_z = .02283, \quad \epsilon_t = .02277;$$

and hence for the probable errors

$$r_x = .01800, \quad r_y = .01855, \quad r_z = .01539, \quad r_t = .01536.$$

$\log \alpha_1^{\;2}$ $\log \alpha_2^{\;2}$ $\log \alpha_3^{\;2}$	$\log \beta_2^{\;2}$ $\log \beta_3^{\;2}$	$\log \gamma_3^{\;2}$	
$\dfrac{1}{[aa]}$ $\dfrac{\alpha_1^{\;2}}{[bb,\,1]}$ $\dfrac{\alpha_2^{\;2}}{[cc,\,2]}$ $\dfrac{\alpha_3^{\;2}}{[dd,\,3]}$	$\dfrac{1}{[bb,\,1]}$ $\dfrac{\beta_2^{\;2}}{[cc,\,2]}$ $\dfrac{\beta_3^{\;2}}{[dd,\,3]}$	$\dfrac{1}{[cc,\,2]}$ $\dfrac{\gamma_3^{\;2}}{[dd,\,3]}$	$\log \dfrac{1}{[aa]}$ $\log \dfrac{1}{[bb,\,1]}$ $\log \dfrac{1}{[cc,\,2]}$ $\log \dfrac{1}{[dd,\,3]}$
$\dfrac{1}{p_x}$ $\log \dfrac{1}{p_x}$	$\dfrac{1}{p_y}$ $\log \dfrac{1}{p_y}$	$\dfrac{1}{p_z}$ $\log \dfrac{1}{p_z}$	$\dfrac{1}{p_t}$ $\log \dfrac{1}{p_t}$
8.53146 7.54462 3.82974	7.38328 4.81444	7.39440	
.32034 .01201 .00085 .00000	.35318 .00059 .00000	.24315 .00060	9.50561 9.54800 9.38587 9.38483
.33320 9.52270	.35377 9.54872	.24375 9.38694	9.38483

Examples.

1. Show that the values of p_z when there are four unknown quantities given in Arts. 158 and 176 are identical.

2. Show that the weight of the determination of $[bn]$ is $[bb]$, that of $[bn, 1]$ is $[bb, 1]$, and so on.

3. Show that, if the normal equation for x were known to be exactly true, the values of the unknown quantities and the weights relatively to that of an observation of all except x would be unchanged, and that the weight of an observation would be increased in the ratio $m - \mu + 1 : m - \mu$.

4. Solve the following normal equations which resulted from twelve observation equations :

$$5.1143x - 0.2792y + 3.3460z = -0.7365,$$
$$- 0.2792x + 14.6142y + 0.1958z = 2.1609,$$
$$3.3460x + 0.1958y + 7.6754z = -0.8927,$$
$$[nn] = 0.5379,$$

and find the probable errors of the unknown quantities.

$$x = -.0803, \quad y = .1475, \quad z = .0851;$$
$$r_x = .034, \quad r_y = .017, \quad r_z = .028.$$

5. Solve the normal equations

$$5.2485x - 1.7472y - 2.1954z = -0.5399,$$
$$- 1.7472y + 1.8859y + 0.8041z = 1.4493,$$
$$- 2.1954y + 0.8041y + 4.0440z = 1.8681,$$
$$[nn] = 2.6322;$$

and given $m = 10$, find the probable errors.

$$[vv] = 0.5504, \quad x = 0.422, \quad y = 0.945, \quad z = 0.503;$$
$$r = 0.189, \quad r_x = 0.108, \quad r_y = 0.166, \quad r_z = 0.107.$$

6. Show that the observation equations

$$0.707x + 2.052y - 2.372z - 0.221t = -\ 6.58,$$
$$0.471x + 1.347y - 1.715z - 0.085t = -\ 1.63,$$
$$0.260x + 0.770y - 0.356z + 0.483t = \ \ \ 4.40,$$
$$0.092x + 0.343y + 0.235z + 0.469t = \ \ 10.21,$$
$$0.414x + 1.204y - 1.506z - 0.205t = -\ 3.99,$$
$$0.040x + 0.150y + 0.104z + 0.206t = \ \ \ 4.34,$$

give rise to the normal equations

$$0.971x + 2.821y - \ \ 3.175z - 0.104t = -\ \ 4.815,$$
$$2.821x + 8.208y - \ \ 9.168z - 0.251t = -\ 12.961,$$
$$-\ 3.175x - 9.168y + 11.028z + 0.938t = \ \ 25.697,$$
$$-\ 0.104x - 0.251y + \ \ 0.938z + 0.594t = \ \ 10.218,$$

and to $[nn] = 204.313$. Determine the unknown quantities and the probable errors of an observation.

$$x = -\ 86.41,\ y = 25.18,\ z = -\ 3.12,\ t = 17.66,\ r = 1.80.$$

7. Account for the small values of the weights, especially of x and y, in Ex. 6. Show directly from the value of $[bb, 1]$ that $p_y < .012$ and $p_x' < .0015$.

8. Ten observation equations gave the normal equations

$$2.02530x + 0.63809y - \ \ 3.99285z = -\ 30.466,$$
$$0.63809x + 0.21649y - \ \ 1.12089z = -\ 11.959,$$
$$-\ 3.99285x - 1.12089y + 10.00000z = -\ 6.000,$$

together with $[nn] = 24928.$; find the values and weights of the unknown quantities and the probable errors.

$$x = -\,202.8, \quad y = 286.3, \quad z = -\,49.5;$$
$$p_x = \quad .0314, \quad p_y = .0066, \quad p_z = \quad .9119;$$
$$r = 37.702, \quad r_x = \quad 213, \quad r_y = 463, \quad r_z = \quad 39.$$

9. Given the following observation equations of equal weight:

$$.986x + .056y = .000, \qquad .953x + .182y = \quad 1.060,$$
$$.973x + .103y = .530, \qquad .943x + .219y = -\,.380.$$
$$.968x + .123y = .680, \qquad .919x + .307y = \quad .200,$$
$$.959x + .157y = .200, \qquad .916x + .317y = -\,.530,$$
$$.912x + 331y = .000,$$

find the normal equations and the value of $[nn]$ by the method
of Art. 127. (Notice that when we put $a + b + n + s = 0$ as
in Art. 169 a considerable saving of labor results from the
fact that $\Sigma(a+b)^2 = \Sigma(n+s)^2$, etc.)

$$8.0884x + 1.6798y = 1.7160,$$
$$1.6798x + 0.4383y = 0.1725,$$
$$[nn] = 2.3722.$$

10. Solve the normal equations found in Ex. 9.

$$x = 0.642, \quad y = -\,2.07, \quad r_x = 0.25, \quad r_y = 1.09.$$

11. Thirteen observation equations give the normal equa‑
tions

$$17.50x - 6.50y - 6.50z = \quad 2.14,$$
$$-\,6.50x + 17.50y - 6.50z = \quad 13.96,$$
$$-\,6.50x - 6.50y + 20.50z = -\,5.40,$$
$$[nn] = \quad 100.34;$$

find the values and probable errors of the unknown quantities.

$$x = 0.67 \pm 0.60, \quad y = 1.17 \pm 0.60, \quad z = 0.32 \pm 0.55.$$

12. Solve the normal equations

$$459x - 308y - 389z + 244t = \quad 507,$$
$$- 308x + 464y + 408z - 269t = - \quad 695,$$
$$- 389x + 408y + 676z - 331t = - \quad 653,$$
$$244x - 269y - 331z + 469t = \quad 283,$$
$$[nn] = \quad 1129.$$

$x = -0.212,\ y = -1.471,\ z = -0.195,\ t = -0.488;$
$[vv] = 10;\ p_x = 207,\quad p_y = 186,\quad p_z = 250,\quad p_t = 281.$

Constants.

$$\rho = 0.4769352, \qquad \log \rho = 9.6784603;$$
$$\rho\sqrt{2} = 0.6744897, \quad \log \rho\sqrt{2} = 9.8289753;$$
$$\rho\sqrt{\pi} = 0.8453475, \quad \log \rho\sqrt{\pi} = 8.9270353;$$
$$r = \rho\sqrt{2} \ .\ \epsilon = \rho\sqrt{\pi} \ .\ \eta.$$

Note that $\rho\sqrt{2} = \alpha + \beta + \gamma + \delta + \ldots$, where $\alpha = \frac{2}{3}$, $\beta = \frac{1}{100}\alpha,\ \ \gamma = \frac{1}{6}\beta,\ \ \delta = \frac{4}{100}\gamma.$

VALUES OF THE PROBABILITY INTEGRAL,

OR PROBABILITY OF AN ERROR NUMERICALLY LESS THAN x.

TABLE I.—VALUES OF P_t.

$$t = hx; \quad P_t = \frac{2}{\sqrt{\pi}} \int_0^t e^{-t^2} dt = \frac{2}{\sqrt{\pi}} \operatorname{Erf} t.$$

t	0	1	2	3	4	5	6	7	8	9
0.0	0.0000	0.0113	0.0226	0.0338	0.0451	0.0564	0.0676	0.0789	0.0901	0.1013
0.1	1125	1236	1348	1459	1569	1680	1790	1900	2009	2118
0.2	2227	2335	2443	2550	2657	2763	2869	2974	3079	3183
0.3	0.3286	0.3389	0.3491	0.3593	0.3694	0.3794	0.3893	0.3992	0.4090	0.4187
0.4	4284	4380	4475	4569	4662	4755	4847	4937	5027	5117
0.5	5205	5292	5379	5465	5549	5633	5716	5798	5879	5959
0.6	0.6039	0.6117	0.6194	0.6270	0.6346	0.6420	0.6494	0.6566	0.6638	0.6708
0.7	6778	6847	6914	6981	7047	7112	7175	7238	7300	7361
0.8	7421	7480	7538	7595	7651	7707	7761	7814	7867	7918
0.9	0.7969	0.8019	0.8068	0.8116	0.8163	0.8209	0.8254	0.8299	0.8342	0.8385
1.0	8427	8468	8508	8548	8586	8624	8661	8698	8733	8768
1.1	8802	8835	8868	8900	8931	8961	8991	9020	9048	9076
1.2	0.9103	0.9130	0.9155	0.9181	0.9205	0.9229	0.9252	0.9275	0.9297	0.9319
1.3	9340	9361	9381	9400	9419	9438	9456	9473	9490	9507
1.4	9523	9539	9554	9569	9583	9597	9611	9624	9637	9649
1.5	0.9661	0.9673	0.9684	0.9695	0.9706	0.9716	0.9726	0.9736	0.9745	0.9755
1.6	9763	9772	9780	9788	9796	9804	9811	9818	9825	9832
1.7	9838	9844	9850	9856	9861	9867	9872	9877	9882	9886
1.8	0.9891	0.9895	0.9899	0.9903	0.9907	0.9911	0.9915	0.9918	0.9922	0.9925
1.9	9928	9931	9934	9937	9939	9942	9944	9947	9949	9951
2.0	9953	9955	9957	9959	9961	9963	9964	9966	9967	9969
2.1	0.9970	0.9972	0.9973	0.9974	0.9975	0.9976	0.9977	0.9979	0.9980	0.9980
2.2	9981	9982	9983	9984	9985	9985	9986	9987	9987	9988
2.3	9989	9989	9990	9990	9991	9991	9992	9992	9992	9993
2.4	0.9993	0.9993	0.9994	0.9994	0.9994	0.9995	0.9995	0.9995	0.9995	0.9996
2.5	9996	9996	9996	9997	9997	9997	9997	9997	9997	9998
2.6	9998	9998	9998	9998	9998	9998	9998	9998	9998	9999
2.7	...	...	...	...	...	...	...	...	...	...
2.8	...	...	...	...	...	...	0.9999	1.0000	...	...

TABLE II.—VALUES OF P_z.

$$z = \frac{x}{r} = \frac{t}{\rho}; \quad P_z = \frac{2}{\sqrt{\pi}} \,\text{Erf}\, \rho z = \frac{2}{\sqrt{\pi}} \int_0^{\rho z} e^{-t^2} dt.$$

z	0	1	2	3	4	5	6	7	8	9
0.0	0.0000	0.0054	0.0108	0.0161	0.0215	0.0269	0.0323	0.0377	0.0430	0.0484
0.1	0538	0591	0645	0699	0752	0806	0859	0913	0966	1020
0.2	1073	1126	118c	1233	1286	1339	139.	1445	1498	1551
0.3	0.1604	0.1656	0.1709	0.1761	0.1814	0.1866	0.1919	0.1971	0.2023	0.2075
0.4	2127	2179	2230	2282	2334	2385	2436	2488	2539	2590
0.5	2641	2691	2742	2793	2843	2893	2944	2994	3044	3093
0.6	0.3143	0.3192	0.3242	0.3291	0.3340	0.3389	0.3438	0.3487	0.3535	0.3584
0.7	3632	3680	3728	3775	3823	3871	3918	3965	4012	4059
0.8	4105	4152	4198	4244	4290	4336	4381	4427	4472	4517
0.9	0.4562	0.4606	0.4651	0.4695	0.4739	0.4783	0.4827	0.4871	0.4914	0.4957
1.0	5000	5043	5085	5128	5170	5212	5254	5295	5337	5378
1.1	5419	5460	5500	5540	5581	5621	5660	5700	5739	5778
1.2	0.5817	0.5856	0.5894	0.5932	0.5971	0.6008	0.6046	0.6083	0.6121	0.6157
1.3	6194	6231	6267	6303	6339	6375	6410	6445	6480	6515
1.4	6550	6584	6618	6652	6686	6719	6753	6786	6818	6851
1.5	0.6883	0.6915	0.6947	0.6979	0.7011	0.7042	0.7073	0.7104	0.7134	0.7165
1.6	7195	7225	7255	7284	7313	7343	7371	7400	7428	7457
1.7	7485	7512	7540	7567	7594	7621	7648	7675	7701	7727
1.8	0.7753	0.7778	0.7804	0.7829	0.7854	0.7879	0.7904	0.7928	0.7952	0.7976
1.9	8000	8023	8047	8070	8093	8116	8138	8161	8183	8205
2.0	8227	8248	8270	8291	8312	8332	8353	8373	8394	8414
2.1	0.8433	0.8453	0.8473	0.8492	0.8511	0.8530	0.8549	0.8567	0.8585	0.8604
2.2	8622	8639	8657	8674	8692	8709	8726	8743	8759	8776
2.3	8792	8808	8824	8839	8855	8870	8886	8901	8916	8930
2.4	0.8945	0.8959	0.8974	0.8988	0.9002	0.9016	0.9029	0.9043	0.9056	0.9069
2.5	9082	9 95	9108	9121	9133	9146	9158	9170	9182	9194
2.6	9205	9217	9228	9239	9250	9261	9272	9283	9293	9304
2.7	0.9314	0.9324	0.9334	0.9344	0.9354	0.9364	0.9373	0.9383	0.9392	0.9401
2.8	9411	9419	9428	9437	9446	9454	9463	9471	9479	9487
2.9	9495	9503	9511	9519	9526	9534	9541	9548	9556	9563
3.0	0.9570	0.9577	0.9583	0.9590	0.9597	0.9603	0.9610	0.9616	0.9622	0.9629
3.1	9635	9641	9647	9652	9658	9664	9669	9675	9680	9686
3.2	9691	9696	9701	9706	9711	9716	9721	9726	9731	9735
3.3	0.9740	0.9744	0.9749	0.9753	0.9757	0.9762	0.9766	0.9770	0.9774	0.9778
3.4	9782	9786	9789	9793	9797	9800	9804	9807	9811	9814
3.	9570	9635	9691	9740	9782	9818	9848	9874	9896	9915
4.	0.9930	0.9943	0.9954	0.9963	0.9970	0.9976	0.9981	0.9985	0.9988	0.9991
5.	9993	9994	9995	9996	9997	9998	9998	9999	9999	9999
6.	9999	1.0000	...	...	...	...	...	...	...	...

Number	Square.	Cube.	Square Root.	Cube Root.
1	1	1	1.0000	1.0000
2	4	8	1.4142	1.2599
3	9	27	1.7321	1.4422
4	16	64	2.0000	1.5874
5	25	125	2.2361	1.7100
6	36	216	2.4495	1.8171
7	49	343	2.6458	1.9129
8	64	512	2.8284	2.0000
9	81	729	3.0000	2.0801
10	1 00	1 000	3.1623	2.1544
11	1 21	1 331	3.3166	2.2240
12	1 44	1 728	3.4641	2.2894
13	1 69	2 197	3.6056	2.3513
14	1 96	2 744	3.7417	2.4101
15	2 25	3 375	3.8730	2.4662
16	2 56	4 096	4.0000	2.5198
17	2 89	4 913	4.1231	2.5713
18	3 24	5 832	4.2426	2.6207
19	3 61	6 859	4.3589	2.6684
20	4 00	8 000	4.4721	2.7144
21	4 41	9 261	4.5826	2.7589
22	4 84	10 648	4.6904	2.8020
23	5 29	12 167	4.7958	2.8439
24	5 76	13 824	4.8990	2.8845
25	6 25	15 625	5.0000	2.9240
26	6 76	17 576	5.0990	2.9625
27	7 29	19 683	5.1962	3.0000
28	7 84	21 952	5.2915	3.0366
29	8 41	24 389	5 3852	3.0723
30	9 00	27 000	5.4772	3.1072
31	9 61	29 791	5.5678	3.1414
32	10 24	32 768	5.6569	3.1748
33	10 89	35 937	5.7446	3.2075
34	11 56	39 304	5.8310	3.2396
35	12 25	42 875	5.9161	3 2711
36	12 96	46 656	6.0000	3.3019
37	13 69	50 653	6.0828	3.3322
38	14 44	54 872	6.1644	3.3620
39	15 21	59 319	6.2450	3.3912
40	16 00	64 000	6.3246	3.4200
41	16 81	68 921	6.4031	3.4482
42	17 64	74 088	6.4807	3.4760
43	18 49	79 507	6.5574	3.5034
44	19 36	85 184	6.6332	3.5303
45	20 25	91 125	6.7082	3.5569
46	21 16	97 336	6.7823	3.5830
47	22 09	103 823	6.8557	3.6088
48	23 04	110 592	6.9282	3.6342
49	24 01	117 649	7.0000	3.6593
50	25 00	125 000	7.0711	3.6840

Number	Square.	Cube.	Square Root.	Cube Root.
51	26 01	132 651	7.1414	3.7084
52	27 04	140 608	7.2111	3.7325
53	28 09	148 877	7.2801	3.7563
54	29 16	157 464	7.3485	3 7798
55	30 25	166 375	7.4162	3.8030
56	31 36	175 616	7.4833	3.8259
57	32 49	185 193	7.5498	3.8485
58	33 64	195 112	7.6158	3.8709
59	34 81	205 379	7.6811	3.8930
60	36 00	216 000	7.7460	3.9149
61	37 21	226 981	7.8102	3.9365
62	38 44	238 328	7.8740	3.9579
63	39 69	250 047	7.9373	3.9791
64	40 96	262 144	8.0000	4.0000
65	42 25	274 625	8.0623	4.0207
66	43 56	287 496	8.1240	4.0412
67	44 89	300 763	8.1854	4.0615
68	46 24	314 432	8.2462	4.0817
69	47 61	328 509	8.3066	4.1016
70	49 00	343 000	8.3666	4.1213
71	50 41	357 911	8.4261	4.1408
72	51 84	373 248	8.4853	4.1602
73	53 29	389 017	8.5440	4.1793
74	54 76	405 224	8.6023	4.1983
75	56 25	421 875	8.6603	4.2172
76	57 76	438 976	8.7178	4.2358
77	59 29	456 533	8.7750	4.2543
78	60 84	474 552	8.8318	4.2727
79	62 41	493 039	8.8882	4.2908
80	64 00	512 000	8.9443	4.3089
81	65 61	531 441	9.0000	4.3267
82	67 24	551 368	9.0554	4.3445
83	68 89	571 787	9.1104	4.3621
84	70 56	592 704	9.1652	4.3795
85	72 25	614 125	9.2195	4.3968
86	73 96	636 056	9.2736	4.4140
87	75 69	658 503	9.3274	4.4310
88	77 44	681 472	9.3808	4.4480
89	79 21	704 969	9.4340	4.4647
90	81 00	729 000	9.4868	4.4814
91	82 81	753 571	9.5394	4.4979
92	84 64	778 688	9.5917	4.5144
93	86 49	804 357	9.6437	4.5307
94	88 36	830 584	9.6954	4.5468
95	90 25	857 375	9.7468	4.5629
96	92 16	884 736	9.7980	4.5789
97	94 09	912 673	9.8489	4.5947
98	96 04	941 192	9.8995	4.6104
99	98 01	970 299	9.9499	4.6261
100	1 00 00	1 000 000	10.0000	4.6416

Number	Square.	Cube.	Square Root.	Cube Root.
101	1 02 01	1 030 301	10.0499	4.6570
102	1 04 04	1 061 208	10.0995	4.6723
103	1 06 09	1 092 727	10.1489	4.6875
104	1 08 16	1 124 864	10.1980	4.7027
105	1 10 25	1 157 625	10.2470	4.7177
106	1 12 36	1 191 016	10.2956	4.7326
107	1 14 49	1 225 043	10.3441	4.7475
108	1 16 64	1 259 712	10.3923	4.7622
109	1 18 81	1 295 029	10.4403	4.7769
110	1 21 00	1 331 000	10.4881	4.7914
111	1 23 21	1 367 631	10.5357	4.8059
112	1 25 44	1 404 928	10.5830	4.8203
113	1 27 69	1 442 897	10.6301	4.8346
114	1 29 96	1 481 544	10.6771	4.8488
115	1 32 25	1 520 875	10.7238	4.8629
116	1 34 56	1 560 896	10.7703	4.8770
117	1 36 89	1 601 613	10.8167	4.8910
118	1 39 24	1 643 032	10.8628	4.9049
119	1 41 61	1 685 159	10.9087	4.9187
120	1 44 00	1 728 000	10.9545	4.9324
121	1 46 41	1 771 561	11.0000	4.9461
122	1 48 84	1 815 848	11.0454	4.9597
123	1 51 29	1 860 867	11.0905	4.9732
124	1 53 76	1 906 624	11.1355	4.9866
125	1 56 25	1 953 125	11.1803	5.0000
126	1 58 76	2 000 376	11.2250	5.0133
127	1 61 29	2 048 383	11.2694	5.0265
128	1 63 84	2 097 152	11.3137	5.0397
129	1 66 41	2 146 689	11.3578	5.0528
130	1 69 00	2 197 000	11.4018	5.0658
131	1 71 61	2 248 091	11.4455	5.0788
132	1 74 24	2 299 968	11.4891	5.0916
133	1 76 89	2 352 637	11.5326	5.1045
134	1 79 56	2 406 104	11.5758	5.1172
135	1 82 25	2 460 375	11.6190	5.1299
136	1 84 96	2 515 456	11.6619	5.1426
137	1 87 69	2 571 353	11.7047	5.1551
138	1 90 44	2 628 072	11.7473	5.1676
139	1 93 21	2 685 619	11.7898	5.1801
140	1 96 00	2 744 000	11.8322	5.1925
141	1 98 81	2 803 221	11.8743	5.2048
142	2 01 64	2 863 288	11.9164	5.2171
143	2 04 49	2 924 207	11.9583	5.2293
144	2 07 36	2 985 984	12.0000	5.2415
145	2 10 25	3 048 625	12.0416	5.2536
146	2 13 16	3 112 136	12.0830	5.2656
147	2 16 09	3 176 523	12.1244	5.2776
148	2 19 04	3 241 792	12.1655	5.2896
149	2 22 01	3 307 949	12.2066	5.3015
150	2 25 00	3 375 000	12.2474	5.3133

Number	Square.	Cube.	Square Root.	Cube Root.
151	2 28 01	3 442 951	12.2882	5.3251
152	2 31 04	3 511 808	12.3288	5.3368
153	2 34 09	3 581 577	12.3693	5.3485
154	2 37 16	3 652 264	12.4097	5.3601
155	2 40 25	3 723 875	12.4499	5.3717
156	2 43 36	3 796 416	12.4900	5.3832
157	2 46 49	3 869 893	12.5300	5.3947
158	2 49 64	3 944 312	12.5698	5.4061
159	2 52 81	4 019 679	12.6095	5.4175
160	2 56 00	4 096 000	12.6491	5.4288
161	2 59 21	4 173 281	12.6886	5.4401
162	2 62 44	4 251 528	12.7279	5.4514
163	2 65 69	4 330 747	12.7671	5.4626
164	2 68 96	4 410 944	12.8062	5.4737
165	2 72 25	4 492 125	12.8452	5.4848
166	2 75 56	4 574 296	12.8841	5.4959
167	2 78 89	4 657 463	12.9228	5.5069
168	2 82 24	4 741 632	12.9615	5.5178
169	2 85 61	4 826 809	13.0000	5.5288
170	2 89 00	4 913 000	13.0384	5.5397
171	2 92 41	5 000 211	13.0767	5.5505
172	2 95 84	5 088 448	13.1149	5.5613
173	2 99 29	5 177 717	13.1529	5.5721
174	3 02 76	5 268 024	13.1909	5.5828
175	3 06 25	5 359 375	13.2288	5.5934
176	3 09 76	5 451 776	13.2665	5.6041
177	3 13 29	5 545 233	13.3041	5.6147
178	3 16 84	5 639 752	13.3417	5.6252
179	3 20 41	5 735 339	13.3791	5.6357
180	3 24 00	5 832 000	13.4164	5.6462
181	3 27 61	5 929 741	13.4536	5.6567
182	3 31 24	6 028 568	13.4907	5.6671
183	3 34 89	6 128 487	13.5277	5.6774
184	3 38 56	6 229 504	13.5647	5.6877
185	3 42 25	6 331 625	13.6015	5.6980
186	3 45 96	6 434 856	13.6382	5.7083
187	3 49 69	6 539 203	13.6748	5.7185
188	3 53 44	6 644 672	13.7113	5.7287
189	3 57 21	6 751 269	13.7477	5.7388
190	3 61 00	6 859 000	13.7840	5.7489
191	3 64 81	6 967 871	13.8203	5.7590
192	3 68 64	7 077 888	13.8564	5.7690
193	3 72 49	7 189 057	13.8924	5.7790
194	3 76 36	7 301 384	13.9284	5.7890
195	3 80 25	7 414 875	13.9642	5.7989
196	3 84 16	7 529 536	14.0000	5.8088
197	3 88 09	7 645 373	14.0357	5.8186
198	3 92 04	7 762 392	14.0712	5.8285
199	3 96 01	7 880 599	14.1067	5.8383
200	4 00 00	8 000 000	14.1421	5.8480

Number	Square.	Cube.	Square Root.	Cube Root.
201	4 04 01	8 120 601	14.1774	5.8578
202	4 08 04	8 242 408	14.2127	5.8675
203	4 12 09	8 365 427	14.2478	5.8771
204	4 16 16	8 489 664	14.2829	5.8868
205	4 20 25	8 615 125	14.3178	5.8964
206	4 24 36	8 741 816	14.3527	5.9059
207	4 28 49	8 869 743	14.3875	5.9155
208	4 32 64	8 998 912	14.4222	5.9250
209	4 36 81	9 129 329	14.4568	5.9345
210	4 41 00	9 261 000	14.4914	5.9439
211	4 45 21	9 393 931	14.5258	5.9533
212	4 49 44	9 528 128	14.5602	5.9627
213	4 53 69	9 663 597	14.5945	5.9721
214	4 57 96	9 800 344	14.6287	5.9814
215	4 62 25	9 938 375	14.6629	5.9907
216	4 66 56	10 077 696	14.6969	6.0000
217	4 70 89	10 218 313	14.7309	6.0092
218	4 75 24	10 360 232	14.7648	6.0185
219	4 79 61	10 503 459	14.7986	6.0277
220	4 84 00	10 648 000	14.8324	6.0368
221	4 88 41	10 793 861	14.8661	6.0459
222	4 92 84	10 941 048	14.8997	6.0550
223	4 97 29	11 089 567	14.9332	6.0641
224	5 01 76	11 239 424	14.9666	6.0732
225	5 06 25	11 390 625	15.0000	6.0822
226	5 10 76	11 543 176	15.0333	6.0912
227	5 15 29	11 697 083	15.0665	6.1002
228	5 19 84	11 852 352	15.0997	6.1091
229	5 24 41	12 008 989	15.1327	6.1180
230	5 29 00	12 167 000	15.1658	6.1269
231	5 33 61	12 326 391	15.1987	6.1358
232	5 38 24	12 487 168	15.2315	6.1446
233	5 42 89	12 649 337	15.2643	6.1534
234	5 47 56	12 812 904	15.2971	6.1622
235	5 52 25	12 977 875	15.3297	6.1710
236	5 56 96	13 144 256	15.3623	6.1797
237	5 61 69	13 312 053	15.3948	6.1885
238	5 66 44	13 481 272	15.4272	6.1972
239	5 71 21	13 651 919	15.4596	6.2058
240	5 76 00	13 824 000	15.4919	6.2145
241	5 80 81	13 997 521	15.5242	6.2231
242	5 85 64	14 172 488	15.5563	6.2317
243	5 90 49	14 348 907	15.5885	6.2403
244	5 95 36	14 526 784	15.6205	6.2488
245	6 00 25	14 706 125	15.6525	6.2573
246	6 05 16	14 886 936	15.6844	6.2658
247	6 10 09	15 069 223	15.7162	6.2743
248	6 15 04	15 252 992	15.7480	6.2828
249	6 20 01	15 438 249	15.7797	6.2912
250	6 25 00	15 625 000	15.8114	6.2996

Number	Square.	Cube.	Square Root.	Cube Root.
251	6 30 01	15 813 251	15.8430	6.3080
252	6 35 04	16 003 008	15.8745	6.3164
253	6 40 09	16 194 277	15.9060	6.3247
254	6 45 16	16 387 064	15.9374	6.3330
255	6 50 25	16 581 375	15.9687	6.3413
256	6 55 36	16 777 216	16.0000	6.3496
257	6 60 49	16 974 593	16.0312	6.3579
258	6 65 64	17 173 512	16.0624	6.3661
259	6 70 81	17 373 979	16.0935	6.3743
260	6 76 00	17 576 000	16.1245	6.3825
261	6 81 21	17 779 581	16.1555	6.3907
262	6 86 44	17 984 728	16.1864	6.3988
263	6 91 69	18 191 447	16.2173	6.4070
264	6 96 96	18 399 744	16.2481	6.4151
265	7 02 25	18 609 625	16.2788	6.4232
266	7 07 56	18 821 096	16.3095	6.4312
267	7 12 89	19 034 163	16.3401	6.4393
268	7 18 24	19 248 832	16.3707	6.4473
269	7 23 61	19 465 109	16.4012	6.4553
270	7 29 00	19 683 000	16.4317	6.4633
271	7 34 41	19 902 511	16.4621	6.4713
272	7 39 84	20 123 648	16.4924	6.4792
273	7 45 29	20 346 417	16.5227	6.4872
274	7 50 76	20 570 824	16.5529	6.4951
275	7 56 25	20 796 875	16.5831	6.5030
276	7 61 76	21 024 576	16.6132	6.5108
277	7 67 29	21 253 933	16.6433	6.5187
278	7 72 84	21 484 952	16.6733	6.5265
279	7 78 41	21 717 639	16.7033	6.5343
280	7 84 00	21 952 000	16.7332	6.5421
281	7 89 61	22 188 041	16.7631	6.5499
282	7 95 24	22 425 768	16.7929	6.5577
283	8 00 89	22 665 187	16.8226	6.5654
284	8 06 56	22 906 304	16.8523	6.5731
285	8 12 25	23 149 125	16.8819	6.5808
286	8 17 96	23 393 656	16.9115	6.5885
287	8 23 69	23 639 903	16.9411	6.5962
288	8 29 44	23 887 872	16.9706	6.6039
289	8 35 21	24 137 569	17.0000	6.6115
290	8 41 00	24 389 000	17.0294	6.6191
291	8 46 81	24 642 171	17.0587	6.6267
292	8 52 64	24 897 088	17.0880	6.6343
293	8 58 49	25 153 757	17.1172	6.6419
294	8 64 36	25 412 184	17.1464	6.6494
295	8 70 25	25 672 375	17.1756	6.6569
296	8 76 16	25 934 336	17.2047	6.6644
297	8 82 09	26 198 073	17.2337	6.6719
298	8 88 04	26 463 592	17.2627	6.6794
299	8 94 01	26 730 899	17.2916	6.6869
300	9 00 00	27 000 000	17.3205	6.6943

Number	Square.	Cube.	Square Root.	Cube Root.
301	9 06 01	27 270 901	17.3494	6.7018
302	9 12 04	27 543 608	17.3781	6.7092
303	9 18 09	27 818 127	17.4069	6.7166
304	9 24 16	28 094 464	17.4356	6.7240
305	9 30 25	28 372 625	17.4642	6.7313
306	9 36 36	28 652 616	17.4929	6.7387
307	9 42 49	28 934 443	17.5214	6.7460
308	9 48 64	29 218 112	17.5499	6.7533
309	9 54 81	29 503 629	17.5784	6.7606
310	9 61 00	29 791 000	17.6068	6.7679
311	9 67 21	30 080 231	17.6352	6.7752
312	9 73 44	30 371 328	17.6635	6.7824
313	9 79 69	30 664 297	17.6918	6.7897
314	9 85 96	30 959 144	17.7200	6.7969
315	9 92 25	31 255 875	17.7482	6.8041
316	9 98 56	31 554 496	17.7764	6.8113
317	10 04 89	31 855 013	17.8045	6.8185
318	10 11 24	32 157 432	17.8326	6.8256
319	10 17 61	32 461 759	17.8606	6.8328
320	10 24 00	32 768 000	17.8885	6.8399
321	10 30 41	33 076 161	17.9165	6.8470
322	10 36 84	33 386 248	17.9444	6.8541
323	10 43 29	33 698 267	17.9722	6.8612
324	10 49 76	34 012 224	18.0000	6.8683
325	10 56 25	34 328 125	18.0278	6.8753
326	10 62 76	34 645 976	18.0555	6.8824
327	10 69 29	34 965 783	18.0831	6.8894
328	10 75 84	35 287 552	18.1108	6.8964
329	10 82 41	35 611 289	18.1384	6.9034
330	10 89 00	35 937 000	18.1659	6.9104
331	10 95 61	36 264 691	18.1934	6.9174
332	11 02 24	36 594 368	18.2209	6.9244
333	11 08 89	36 926 037	18.2483	6.9313
334	11 15 56	37 259 704	18.2757	6.9382
335	11 22 25	37 595 375	18.3030	6.9451
336	11 28 96	37 933 056	18.3303	6.9521
337	11 35 69	38 272 753	18.3576	6.9589
338	11 42 44	38 614 472	18.3848	6.9658
339	11 49 21	38 958 219	18.4120	6.9727
340	11 56 00	39 304 000	18.4391	6.9795
341	11 62 81	39 651 821	18.4662	6.9864
342	11 69 64	40 001 688	18.4932	6.9932
343	11 76 49	40 353 607	18.5203	7.0000
344	11 83 36	40 707 584	18.5472	7.0068
345	11 90 25	41 063 625	18.5742	7.0136
346	11 97 16	41 421 736	18.6011	7.0203
347	12 04 09	41 781 923	18.6279	7.0271
348	12 11 04	42 144 192	18.6548	7.0338
349	12 18 01	42 508 549	18.6815	7.0406
350	12 25 00	42 875 000	18.7083	7.0473

Number	Square.	Cube.	Square Root.	Cube Root.
351	12 32 01	43 243 551	18.7350	7.0540
352	12 39 04	43 614 208	18.7617	7.0607
353	12 46 09	43 986 977	18.7883	7.0674
354	12 53 16	44 361 864	18.8149	7.0740
355	12 60 25	44 738 875	18.8414	7.0807
356	12 67 36	45 118 016	18.8680	7.0873
357	12 74 49	45 499 293	18.8944	7.0940
358	12 81 64	45 882 712	18.9209	7.1006
359	12 88 81	46 268 279	18.9473	7.1072
360	12 96 00	46 656 000	18.9737	7.1138
361	13 03 21	47 045 881	19.0000	7.1204
362	13 10 44	47 437 928	19.0263	7.1269
363	13 17 69	47 832 147	19.0526	7.1335
364	13 24 96	48 228 544	19.0788	7.1400
365	13 32 25	48 627 125	19.1050	7.1466
366	13 39 56	49 027 896	19.1311	7.1531
367	13 46 89	49 430 863	19.1572	7.1596
368	13 54 24	49 836 032	19.1833	7.1661
369	13 61 61	50 243 409	19.2094	7.1726
370	13 69 00	50 653 000	19.2354	7.1791
371	13 76 41	51 064 811	19.2614	7.1855
372	13 83 84	51 478 848	19.2873	7.1920
373	13 91 29	51 895 117	19.3132	7.1984
374	13 98 76	52 313 624	19.3391	7.2048
375	14 06 25	52 734 375	19.3649	7.2112
376	14 13 76	53 157 376	19.3907	7.2177
377	14 21 29	53 582 633	19.4165	7.2240
378	14 28 84	54 010 152	19.4422	7.2304
379	14 36 41	54 439 939	19.4679	7.2368
380	14 44 00	54 872 000	19.4936	7.2432
381	14 51 61	55 306 341	19.5192	7.2495
382	14 59 24	55 742 968	19.5448	7.2558
383	14 66 89	56 181 887	19.5704	7.2622
384	14 74 56	56 623 104	19.5959	7.2685
385	14 82 25	57 066 625	19.6214	7.2748
386	14 89 96	57 512 456	19.6469	7.2811
387	14 97 69	57 960 603	19.6723	7.2874
388	15 05 44	58 411 072	19.6977	7.2936
389	15 13 21	58 863 869	19.7231	7.2999
390	15 21 00	59 319 000	19.7484	7.3061
391	15 28 81	59 776 471	19.7737	7.3124
392	15 36 64	60 236 288	19.7990	7.3186
393	15 44 49	60 698 457	19.8242	7.3248
394	15 52 36	61 162 984	19.8494	7.3310
395	15 60 25	61 629 875	19.8746	7.3372
396	15 68 16	62 099 136	19.8997	7.3434
397	15 76 09	62 570 773	19.9249	7.3496
398	15 84 04	63 044 792	19.9499	7.3558
399	15 92 01	63 521 199	19.9750	7.3619
400	16 00 00	64 000 000	20.0000	7.3681

Number	Square.	Cube.	Square Root.	Cube Root.
401	16 08 01	64 481 201	20.0250	7.3742
402	16 16 04	64 964 808	20.0499	7.3803
403	16 24 09	65 450 827	20.0749	7.3864
404	16 32 16	65 939 264	20.0998	7.3925
405	16 40 25	66 430 125	20.1246	7.3986
406	16 48 36	66 923 416	20.1494	7.4047
407	16 56 49	67 419 143	20.1742	7.4108
408	16 64 64	67 917 312	20.1990	7.4169
409	16 72 81	68 417 929	20.2237	7.4229
410	16 81 00	68 921 000	20.2485	7.4290
411	16 89 21	69 426 531	20.2731	7.4350
412	16 97 44	69 934 528	20.2978	7.4410
413	17 05 69	70 444 997	20.3224	7.4470
414	17 13 96	70 957 944	20.3470	7.4530
415	17 22 25	71 473 375	20.3715	7.4590
416	17 30 56	71 991 296	20.3961	7.4650
417	17 38 89	72 511 713	20.4206	7.4710
418	17 47 24	73 034 632	20.4450	7.4770
419	17 55 61	73 560 059	20.4695	7.4829
420	17 64 00	74 088 000	20.4939	7.4889
421	17 72 41	74 618 461	20.5183	7.4948
422	17 80 84	75 151 448	20.5426	7.5007
423	17 89 29	75 686 967	20.5670	7.5067
424	17 97 76	76 225 024	20.5913	7.5126
425	18 06 25	76 765 625	20.6155	7.5185
426	18 14 76	77 308 776	20.6398	7.5244
427	18 23 29	77 854 483	20.6640	7.5302
428	18 31 84	78 402 752	20.6882	7.5361
429	18 40 41	78 953 589	20.7123	7.5420
430	18 49 00	79 507 000	20.7364	7.5478
431	18 57 61	80 062 991	20.7605	7.5537
432	18 66 24	80 621 568	20.7846	7.5595
433	18 74 89	81 182 737	20.8087	7.5654
434	18 83 56	81 746 504	20.8327	7.5712
435	18 92 25	82 312 875	20.8567	7.5770
436	19 00 96	82 881 856	20.8806	7.5828
437	19 09 69	83 453 453	20.9045	7.5886
438	19 18 44	84 027 672	20.9284	7.5944
439	19 27 21	84 604 519	20.9523	7.6001
440	19 36 00	85 184 000	20.9762	7.6059
441	19 44 81	85 766 121	21.0000	7.6117
442	19 53 64	86 350 888	21.0238	7.6174
443	19 62 49	86 938 307	21.0476	7.6232
444	19 71 36	87 528 384	21.0713	7.6289
445	19 80 25	88 121 125	21.0950	7.6346
446	19 89 16	88 716 536	21.1187	7.6403
447	19 98 09	89 314 623	21.1424	7.6460
448	20 07 04	89 915 392	21.1660	7.6517
449	20 16 01	90 518 849	21.1896	7.6574
450	20 25 00	91 125 000	21.2132	7.6631

Number	Square.	Cube.	Square Root.	Cube Root.
451	20 34 01	91 733 851	21.2368	7.6688
452	20 43 04	92 345 408	21.2603	7.6744
453	20 52 09	92 959 677	21.2838	7.6801
454	20 61 16	93 576 664	21.3073	7.6857
455	20 70 25	94 196 375	21.3307	7.6914
456	20 79 36	94 818 816	21.3542	7.6970
457	20 88 49	95 443 993	21.3776	7.7026
458	20 97 64	96 071 912	21.4009	7.7082
459	21 06 81	96 702 579	21.4243	7.7138
460	21 16 00	97 336 000	21.4476	7.7194
461	21 25 21	97 972 181	21.4709	7.7250
462	21 34 44	98 611 128	21.4942	7.7306
463	21 43 69	99 252 847	21.5174	7.7362
464	21 52 96	99 897 344	21.5407	7.7418
465	21 62 25	100 544 625	21.5639	7.7473
466	21 71 56	101 194 696	21.5870	7.7529
467	21 80 89	101 847 563	21.6102	7.7584
468	21 90 24	102 503 232	21.6333	7.7639
469	21 99 61	103 161 709	21.6564	7.7695
470	22 09 00	103 823 000	21.6795	7.7750
471	22 18 41	104 487 111	21.7025	7.7805
472	22 27 84	105 154 048	21.7256	7.7860
473	22 37 29	105 823 817	21.7486	7.7915
474	22 46 76	106 496 424	21.7715	7.7970
475	22 56 25	107 171 875	21.7945	7.8025
476	22 65 76	107 850 176	21.8174	7.8079
477	22 75 29	108 531 333	21.8403	7.8134
478	22 84 84	109 215 352	21.8632	7.8188
479	22 94 41	109 902 239	21.8861	7.8243
480	23 04 00	110 592 000	21.9089	7.8297
481	23 13 61	111 284 641	21.9317	7.8352
482	23 23 24	111 980 168	21.9545	7.8406
483	23 32 89	112 678 587	21.9773	7.8460
484	23 42 56	113 379 904	22.0000	7.8514
485	23 52 25	114 084 125	22.0227	7.8568
486	23 61 96	114 791 256	22.0454	7.8622
487	23 71 69	115 501 303	22.0681	7.8676
488	23 81 44	116 214 272	22.0907	7.8730
489	23 91 21	116 930 169	22.1133	7.8784
490	24 01 00	117 649 000	22.1359	7.8837
491	24 10 81	118 370 771	22.1585	7.8891
492	24 20 64	119 095 488	22.1811	7.8944
493	24 30 49	119 823 157	22.2036	7.8998
494	24 40 36	120 553 784	22.2261	7.9051
495	24 50 25	121 287 375	22.2486	7.9105
496	24 60 16	122 023 936	22.2711	7.9158
497	24 70 09	122 763 473	22.2935	7.9211
498	24 80 04	123 505 992	22.3159	7.9264
499	24 90 01	124 251 499	22.3383	7.9317
500	25 00 00	125 000 000	22.3607	7.9370

Number	Square.	Cube.	Square Root.	Cube Root.
501	25 10 01	125 751 501	22.3830	7.9423
502	25 20 04	126 506 008	22.4054	7.9476
503	25 30 09	127 263 527	22.4277	7.9528
504	25 40 16	128 024 064	22.4499	7.9581
505	25 50 25	128 787 625	22.4722	7.9634
506	25 60 36	129 554 216	22.4944	7.9686
507	25 70 49	130 323 843	22.5167	7.9739
508	25 80 63	131 096 512	22.5389	7.9791
509	25 90 81	131 872 229	22.5610	7.9843
510	26 01 00	132 651 000	22.5832	7.9896
511	26 11 21	133 432 831	22.6053	7.9948
512	26 21 44	134 217 728	22.6274	8.0000
513	26 31 69	135 005 697	22.6495	8.0052
514	26 41 96	135 796 744	22.6716	8.0104
515	26 52 25	136 590 875	22.6936	8.0156
516	26 62 56	137 388 096	22.7156	8.0208
517	26 72 89	138 188 413	22.7376	8.0260
518	26 83 24	138 991 832	22.7596	8.0311
519	26 93 61	139 798 359	22.7816	8.0363
520	27 04 00	140 608 000	22.8035	8.0415
521	27 14 41	141 420 761	22.8254	8.0466
522	27 24 84	142 236 648	22.8473	8.0517
523	27 35 29	143 055 667	22.8692	8.0569
524	27 45 76	143 877 824	22.8910	8.0620
525	27 56 25	144 703 125	22.9129	8.0671
526	27 66 76	145 531 576	22.9347	8.0723
527	27 77 29	146 363 183	22.9565	8.0774
528	27 87 84	147 197 952	22.9783	8.0825
529	27 98 41	148 035 889	23.0000	8.0876
530	28 09 00	148 877 000	23.0217	8.0927
531	28 19 61	149 721 291	23.0434	8.0978
532	28 30 24	150 568 768	23.0651	8.1028
533	28 40 89	151 419 437	23.0868	8.1079
534	28 51 56	152 273 304	23.1084	8.1130
535	28 62 25	153 130 375	23.1301	8.1180
536	28 72 96	153 990 656	23.1517	8.1231
537	28 83 69	154 854 153	23.1733	8.1281
538	28 94 44	155 720 872	23.1948	8.1332
539	29 05 21	156 590 819	23.2164	8.1382
540	29 16 00	157 464 000	23.2379	8.1433
541	29 26 81	158 340 421	23.2594	8.1483
542	29 37 64	159 220 088	23.2809	8.1533
543	29 48 49	160 103 007	23.3024	8.1583
544	29 59 36	160 989 184	23.3238	8.1633
545	29 70 25	161 878 625	23.3452	8.1683
546	29 81 16	162 771 336	23.3666	8.1733
547	29 92 09	163 667 323	23.3880	8.1783
548	30 03 04	164 566 592	23.4094	8.1833
549	30 14 01	165 469 149	23.4307	8.1882
550	30 25 00	166 375 000	23.4521	8.1932

Number	Square.	Cube.	Square Root.	Cube Root.
551	30 36 01	167 284 151	23.4734	8.1982
552	30 47 04	168 196 608	23.4947	8.2031
553	30 58 09	169 112 377	23.5160	8.2081
554	30 69 16	170 031 464	23.5372	8.2130
555	30 80 25	170 953 875	23.5584	8.2180
556	30 91 36	171 879 616	23.5797	8.2229
557	31 02 49	172 808 693	23.6008	8.2278
558	31 13 64	173 741 112	23.6220	8.2327
559	31 24 81	174 676 879	23.6432	8.2377
560	31 36 00	175 616 000	23.6643	8.2426
561	31 47 21	176 558 481	23.6854	8.2475
562	31 58 44	177 504 328	23.7065	8.2524
563	31 69 69	178 453 547	23.7276	8.2573
564	31 80 96	179 406 144	23.7487	8.2621
565	31 92 25	180 362 125	23.7697	8.2670
566	32 03 56	181 321 496	23.7908	8.2719
567	32 14 89	182 284 263	23.8118	8.2768
568	32 26 24	183 250 432	23.8328	8.2816
569	32 37 61	184 220 009	23.8537	8.2865
570	32 49 00	185 193 000	23.8747	8.2913
571	32 60 41	186 169 411	23.8956	8.2962
572	32 71 84	187 149 248	23.9165	8.3010
573.	32 83 29	188 132 517	23.9374	8.3059
574	32 94 76	189 119 224	23.9583	8.3107
575	33 06 25	190 109 375	23.9792	8.3155
576	33 17 76	191 102 976	24.0000	8.3203
577	33 29 29	192 100 033	24.0208	8.3251
578	33 40 84	193 100 552	24.0416	8.3300
579	33 52 41	194 104 539	24.0624	8.3348
580	33 64 00	195 112 000	24.0832	8.3396
581	33 75 61	196 122 941	24.1039	8.3443
582	33 87 24	197 137 368	24.1247	8.3491
583	33 98 89	198 155 287	24.1454	8.3539
584	34 10 56	199 176 704	24.1661	8.3587
585	34 22 25	200 201 625	24.1868	8.3634
586	34 33 96	201 230 056	24.2074	8.3682
587	34 45 69	202 262 003	24.2281	8.3730
588	34 57 44	203 297 472	24.2487	8.3777
589	34 69 21	204 336 469	24.2693	8.3825
590	34 81 00	205 379 000	24.2899	8.3872
591	34 92 81	206 425 071	24.3105	8.3919
592	35 04 64	207 474 688	24.3311	8.3967
593	35 16 49	208 527 857	24.3516	8.4014
594	35 28 36	209 584 584	24.3721	8.4061
595	35 40 25	210 644 875	24.3926	8.4108
596	35 52 16	211 708 736	24.4131	8.4155
597	35 64 09	212 776 173	24.4336	8.4202
598	35 76 04	213 847 192	24.4540	8.4249
599	35 88 01	214 921 799	24.4745	8.4296
600	36 00 00	216 000 000	24.4949	8.4343

Number	Square.	Cube.	Square Root.	Cube Root.
601	36 12 01	217 081 801	24.5153	8.4390
602	36 24 04	218 167 208	24.5357	8.4437
603	36 36 09	219 256 227	24.5561	8.4484
604	36 48 16	220 348 864	24.5764	8.4530
605	36 60 25	221 445 125	24.5967	8.4577
606	36 72 36	222 545 016	24.6171	8.4623
607	36 84 49	223 648 543	24.6374	8.4670
608	36 96 64	224 755 712	24.6577	8.4716
609	37 08 81	225 866 529	24.6779	8.4763
610	37 21 00	226 981 000	24.6982	8.4809
611	37 33 21	228 099 131	24.7184	8.4856
612	37 45 44	229 220 928	24.7386	8.4902
613	37 57 69	230 346 397	24.7588	8.4948
614	37 69 96	231 475 544	24.7790	8.4994
615	37 82 25	232 608 375	24.7992	8.5040
616	37 94 56	233 744 896	24.8193	8.5086
617	38 06 89	234 885 113	24.8395	8.5132
618	38 19 24	236 029 032	24.8596	8.5178
619	38 31 61	237 176 659	24 8797	8.5224
620	38 44 00	238 328 000	24.8998	8.5270
621	38 56 41	239 483 061	24.9199	8.5316
622	38 68 84	240 641 848	24.9399	8.5362
623	38 81 29	241 804 367	24.9600	8.5408
624	38 93 76	242 970 624	24.9800	8.5453
625	39 06 25	244 140 625	25.0000	8 5499
626	39 18 76	245 314 376	25.0200	8.5544
627	39 31 29	246 491 883	25.0400	8.5590
628	39 43 84	247 673 152	25.0599	8.5635
629	39 56 41	248 858 189	25.0799	8.5681
630	39 69 00	250 047 000	25.0998	8.5726
631	39 81 61	251 239 591	25.1197	8.5772
632	39 94 24	252 435 968	25.1396	8.5817
633	40 06 89	253 636 137	25.1595	8.5862
634	40 19 56	254 840 104	25.1794	8.5907
635	40 32 25	256 047 875	25.1992	8.5952
636	40 44 96	257 259 456	25.2190	8.5997
637	40 57 69	258 474 853	25.2389	8.6043
638	40 70 44	259 694 072	25.2587	8.6088
639	40 83 21	260 917 119	25.2784	8.6132
640	40 96 00	262 144 000	25 2982	8.6177
641	41 08 81	263 374 721	25.3180	8.6222
642	41 21 64	264 609 288	25.3377	8.6267
643	41 34 49	265 847 707	25.3574	8.6312
644	41 47 36	267 089 984	25.3772	8.6357
645	41 60 25	268 336 125	25.3969	8.6401
646	41 73 16	269 586 136	25.4165	8 6446
647	41 86 09	270 840 023	25.4362	8.6490
648	41 99 04	272 097 792	25.4558	8.6535
649	42 12 01	273 359 549	25.4755	8.6579
650	42 25 00	274 625 000	25 4951	8.6624

Number.	Square.	Cube.	Square Root.	Cube Root.
651	42 38 01	275 894 451	25.5147	8.6668
652	42 51 04	277 167 808	25.5343	8.6713
653	42 64 09	278 445 077	25.5539	8.6757
654	42 77 16	279 726 264	25.5734	8.6801
655	42 90 25	281 011 375	25.5930	8.6845
656	43 03 36	282 300 416	25.6125	8.6890
657	43 16 49	283 593 393	25.6320	8.6934
658	43 29 64	284 890 312	25.6515	8.6978
659	43 42 81	286 191 179	25.6710	8.7022
660	43 56 00	287 496 000	25.6905	8.7066
661	43 69 21	288 804 781	25.7099	8.7110
662	43 82 44	290 117 528	25.7294	8.7154
663	43 95 69	291 434 247	25.7488	8.7198
664	44 08 96	292 754 944	25.7682	8.7241
665	44 22 25	294 079 625	25.7876	8.7285
666	44 35 56	295 408 296	25.8070	8.7329
667	44 48 89	296 740 963	25.8263	8.7373
668	44 62 24	298 077 632	25.8457	8.7416
669	44 75 61	299 418 309	25.8650	8.7460
670	44 89 00	300 763 000	25.8844	8.7503
671	45 02 41	302 111 711	25.9037	8.7547
672	45 15 84	303 464 448	25.9230	8.7590
673	45 29 29	304 821 217	25.9422	8.7634
674	45 42 76	306 182 024	25.9615	8.7677
675	45 56 25	307 546 875	25.9808	8.7721
676	45 69 76	308 915 776	26.0000	8.7764
677	45 83 29	310 288 733	26.0192	8.7807
678	45 96 84	311 665 752	26.0384	8.7850
679	46 10 41	313 046 839	26.0576	8.7893
680	46 24 00	314 432 000	26.0768	8.7937
681	46 37 61	315 821 241	26.0960	8.7980
682	46 51 24	317 214 568	26.1151	8.8023
683	46 64 89	318 611 987	26.1343	8.8066
684	46 78 56	320 013 504	26.1534	8.8109
685	46 92 25	321 419 125	26.1725	8.8152
686	47 05 96	322 828 856	26.1916	8.8194
687	47 19 69	324 242 703	26.2107	8.8237
688	47 33 44	325 660 672	26.2298	8.8280
689	47 47 21	327 082 769	26.2488	8.8323
690	47 61 00	328 509 000	26.2679	8.8366
691	47 74 81	329 939 371	26.2869	8.8408
692	47 88 64	331 373 888	26.3059	8.8451
693	48 02 49	332 812 557	26.3249	8.8493
694	48 16 36	334 255 384	26.3439	8.8536
695	48 30 25	335 702 375	26.3629	8.8578
696	48 44 16	337 153 536	26.3818	8.8621
697	48 58 09	338 608 873	26.4008	8.8663
698	48 72 04	340 068 392	26.4197	8.8706
699	48 86 01	341 532 099	26.4386	8.8748
700	49 00 00	343 000 000	26.4575	8.8790

Number	Square.	Cube.	Square Root.	Cube Root.
701	49 14 01	344 472 101	26.4764	8.8833
702	49 28 04	345 948 408	26.4953	8.8875
703	49 42 09	347 428 927	26.5141	8.8917
704	49 56 16	348 913 664	26.5330	8.8959
705	49 70 25	350 402 625	26.5518	8.9001
706	49 84 36	351 895 816	26.5707	8.9043
707	49 98 49	353 393 243	26.5895	8.9085
708	50 12 64	354 894 912	26.6083	8.9127
709	50 26 81	356 400 829	26.6271	8.9169
710	50 41 00	357 911 000	26.6458	8.9211
711	50 55 21	359 425 431	26.6646	8.9253
712	50 69 44	360 944 128	26.6833	8.9295
713	50 83 69	362 467 097	26.7021	8.9337
714	50 97 96	363 994 344	26.7208	8.9378
715	51 12 25	365 525 875	26.7395	8.9420
716	51 26 56	367 061 696	26.7582	8.9462
717	51 40 89	368 601 813	26.7769	8.9503
718	51 55 24	370 146 232	26.7955	8.9545
719	51 69 61	371 694 959	26.8142	8.9587
720	51 84 00	373 248 000	26.8328	8.9628
721	51 98 41	374 805 361	26.8514	8.9670
722	52 12 84	376 367 048	26.8701	8.9711
723	52 27 29	377 933 067	26.8887	8.9752
724	52 41 76	379 503 424	26.9072	8.9794
725	52 56 25	381 078 125	26.9258	8.9835
726	52 70 76	382 657 176	26.9444	8.9876
727	52 85 29	384 240 583	26.9629	8.9918
728	52 99 84	385 828 352	26.9815	8.9959
729	53 14 41	387 420 489	27.0000	9.0000
730	53 29 00	389 017 000	27.0185	9.0041
731	53 43 61	390 617 891	27.0370	9.0082
732	53 58 24	392 223 168	27.0555	9.0123
733	53 72 89	393 832 837	27.0740	9.0164
734	53 87 56	395 446 904	27.0924	9.0205
735	54 02 25	397 065 375	27.1109	9.0246
736	54 16 96	398 688 256	27.1293	9.0287
737	54 31 69	400 315 553	27.1477	9.0328
738	54 46 44	401 947 272	27.1662	9.0369
739	54 61 21	403 583 419	27.1846	9.0410
740	54 76 00	405 224 000	27.2029	9.0450
741	54 90 81	406 869 021	27.2213	9.0491
742	55 05 64	408 518 488	27.2397	9.0532
743	55 20 49	410 172 407	27.2580	9.0572
744	55 35 36	411 830 784	27.2764	9.0613
745	55 50 25	413 493 625	27.2947	9.0654
746	55 65 16	415 160 936	27.3130	9.0694
747	55 80 09	416 832 723	27.3313	9.0735
748	55 95 04	418 508 992	27.3496	9.0775
749	56 10 01	420 189 749	27.3679	9.0816
750	56 25 00	421 875 000	27.3861	9.0856

Number	Square.	Cube.	Square Root.	Cube Root.
751	56 40 01	423 564 751	27.4044	9.0896
752	56 55 04	425 259 008	27.4226	9.0937
753	56 70 09	426 957 777	27.4408	9.0977
754	56 85 16	428 661 064	27.4591	9.1017
755	57 00 25	430 368 875	27.4773	9.1057
756	57 15 36	432 081 216	27.4955	9.1098
757	57 30 49	433 798 093	27.5136	9.1138
758	57 45 64	435 519 512	27.5318	9.1178
759	57 60 81	437 245 479	27.5500	9.1218
760	57 76 00	438 976 000	27.5681	9.1258
761	57 91 21	440 711 081	27.5862	9.1298
762	58 06 44	442 450 728	27.6043	9.1338
763	58 21 69	444 194 947	27.6225	9.1378
764	58 36 96	445 943 744	27.6405	9.1418
765	58 52 25	447 697 125	27.6586	9.1458
766	58 67 56	449 455 096	27.6767	9.1498
767	58 82 89	451 217 663	27.6948	9.1537
768	58 98 24	452 984 832	27.7128	9.1577
769	59 13 61	454 756 609	27.7308	9.1617
770	59 29 00	456 533 000	27.7489	9.1657
771	59 44 41	458 314 011	27.7669	9.1696
772	59 59 84	460 099 648	27.7849	9.1736
773	59 75 29	461 889 917	27.8029	9.1775
774	59 90 76	463 684 824	27.8209	9.1815
775	60 06 25	465 484 375	27.8388	9.1855
776	60 21 76	467 288 576	27.8568	9.1894
777	60 37 29	469 097 433	27.8747	9.1933
778	60 52 84	470 910 952	27.8927	9.1973
779	60 68 41	472 729 139	27.9106	9.2012
780	60 84 00	474 552 000	27.9285	9.2052
781	60 99 61	476 379 541	27.9464	9.2091
782	61 15 24	478 211 768	27.9643	9.2130
783	61 30 89	480 048 687	27.9821	9.2170
784	61 46 56	481 890 304	28.0000	9.2209
785	61 62 25	483 736 625	28.0179	9.2248
786	61 77 96	485 587 656	28.0357	9.2287
787	61 93 69	487 443 403	28.0535	9.2326
788	62 09 44	489 303 872	28.0713	9.2365
789	62 25 21	491 169 069	28.0891	9.2404
790	62 41 00	493 039 000	28.1069	9.2443
791	62 56 81	494 913 671	28.1247	9.2482
792	62 72 64	496 793 088	28.1425	9.2521
793	62 88 49	498 677 257	28.1603	9.2560
794	63 04 36	500 566 184	28.1780	9.2599
795	63 20 25	502 459 875	28.1957	9.2638
796	63 36 16	504 358 336	28.2135	9.2677
797	63 52 09	506 261 573	28.2312	9.2716
798	63 68 04	508 169 592	28.2489	9.2754
799	63 84 01	510 082 399	28.2666	9.2793
800	64 00 00	512 000 000	28.2843	9.2832

Number	Square.	Cube.	Square Root.	Cube Root
801	64 16 01	513 922 401	28.3019	9.2870
802	64 32 04	515 849 608	28.3196	9.2909
803	64 48 09	517 781 627	28.3373	9.2948
804	64 64 16	519 718 464	28.3549	9.2986
805	64 80 25	521 660 125	28.3725	9 3025
806	64 96 36	523 606 616	28.3901	9.3063
807	65 12 49	525 557 943	28.4077	9.3102
808	65 28 64	527 514 112	28.4253	9.3140
809	65 44 81	529 475 129	28.4429	9.3179
810	65 61 00	531 441 000	28.4605	9.3217
811	65 77 21	533 411 731	28.4781	9.3255
812	65 93 44	535 387 328	28.4956	9.3294
813	66 09 69	537 367 797	28.5132	9.3332
814	66 25 96	539 353 144	28.5307	9.3370
815	66 42 25	541 343 375	28.5482	9.3408
816	66 58 56	543 338 496	28.5657	9.3447
817	66 74 89	545 338 513	28.5832	9.3485
818	66 91 24	547 343 432	28.6007	9.3523
819	67 07 61	549 353 259	28.6182	9.3561
820	67 24 00	551 368 000	28.6356	9.3599
821	67 40 41	553 387 661	28.6531	9.3637
822	67 56 84	555 412 248	28.6705	9.3675
823	67 73 29	557 441 767	28.6880	9.3713
824	67 89 76	559 476 224	28.7054	9.3751
825	68 06 25	561 515 625	28.7228	9.3789
826	68 22 76	563 559 976	28.7402	9.3827
827	68 39 29	565 609 283	28.7576	9.3865
828	68 55 84	567 663 552	28.7750	9.3902
829	68 72 41	569 722 789	28.7924	9.3940
830	68 89 00	571 787 000	28.8097	9.3978
831	69 05 61	573 856 191	28.8271	9.4016
832	69 22 24	575 930 368	28.8444	9.4053
833	69 38 89	578 009 537	28.8617	9.4091
834	69 55 56	580 093 704	28.8791	9.4129
835	69 72 25	582 182 875	28.8964	9.4166
836	69 88 96	584 277 056	28.9137	9.4204
837	70 05 69	586 376 253	28.9310	9.4241
838	70 22 44	588 480 472	28.9482	9.4279
839	70 39 21	590 589 719	28.9655	9.4316
840	70 56 00	592 704 000	28.9828	9.4354
841	70 72 81	594 823 321	29.0000	9.4391
842	70 89 64	596 947 688	29.0172	9.4429
843	71 06 49	599 077 107	29.0345	9.4466
844	71 23 36	601 211 584	29.0517	9.4503
845	71 40 25	603 351 125	29.0689	9.4541
846	71 57 16	605 495 736	29.0861	9.4578
847	71 74 09	607 645 423	29.1033	9.4615
848	71 91 04	609 800 192	29.1204	9.4652
849	72 08 01	611 960 049	29.1376	9.4690
850	72 25 00	614 125 000	29.1548	9.4727

Number	Square.	Cube.	Square Root.	Cube Root.
851	72 42 01	616 295 051	29.1719	9.4764
852	72 59 04	618 470 208	29.1890	9.4801
853	72 76 09	620 650 477	29.2062	9.4838
854	72 93 16	622 835 864	29.2233	9.4875
855	73 10 25	625 026 375	29.2404	9.4912
856	73 27 36	627 222 016	29.2575	9.4949
857	73 44 49	629 422 793	29.2746	9.4986
858	73 61 64	631 628 712	29.2916	9.5023
859	73 78 81	633 839 779	29.3087	9.5060
860	73 96 00	636 056 000	29.3258	9.5097
861	74 13 21	638 277 381	29.3428	9.5134
862	74 30 44	640 503 928	29.3598	9.5171
863	74 47 69	642 735 647	29.3769	9.5207
864	74 64 96	644 972 544	29.3939	9.5244
865	74 82 25	647 214 625	29.4109	9.5281
866	74 99 56	649 461 896	29.4279	9.5317
867	75 16 89	651 714 363	29.4449	9.5354
868	75 34 24	653 972 032	29.4618	9.5391
869	75 51 61	656 234 909	29.4788	9.5427
870	75 69 00	658 503 000	29.4958	9.5464
871	75 86 41	660 776 311	29.5127	9.5501
872	76 03 84	663 054 848	29.5296	9.5537
873	76 21 29	665 338 617	29.5466	9.5574
874	76 38 76	667 627 624	29.5635	9.5610
875	76 56 25	669 921 875	29.5804	9.5647
876	76 73 76	672 221 376	29.5973	9.5683
877	76 91 29	674 526 133	29.6142	9.5719
878	77 08 84	676 836 152	29.6311	9.5756
879	77 26 41	679 151 439	29.6479	9.5792
880	77 44 00	681 472 000	29.6648	9.5828
881	77 61 61	683 797 841	29.6816	9.5865
882	77 79 24	686 128 968	29.6985	9.5901
883	77 96 89	688 465 387	29.7153	9.5937
884	78 14 56	690 807 104	29.7321	9.5973
885	78 32 25	693 154 125	29.7489	9.6010
886	78 49 96	695 506 456	29.7658	9.6046
887	78 67 69	697 864 103	29.7825	9.6082
888	78 85 44	700 227 072	29.7993	9.6118
889	79 03 21	702 595 369	29.8161	9.6154
890	79 21 00	704 969 000	29.8329	9.6190
891	79 38 81	707 347 971	29.8496	9.6226
892	79 56 64	709 732 288	29.8664	9.6262
893	79 74 49	712 121 957	29.8831	9.6298
894	79 92 36	714 516 984	29.8998	9.6334
895	80 10 25	716 917 375	29.9166	9.6370
896	80 28 16	719 323 136	29.9333	9.6406
897	80 46 09	721 734 273	29.9500	9.6442
898	80 64 04	724 150 792	29.9666	9.6477
899	80 82 01	726 572 699	29.9833	9.6513
900	81 00 00	729 000 000	30.0000	9.6549

Number	Square.	Cube.	Square Root.	Cube Root.
901	81 18 01	731 432 701	30.0167	9.6585
902	81 36 04	733 870 808	30.0333	9.6620
903	81 54 09	736 314 327	30.0500	9.6656
904	81 72 16	738 763 264	30.0666	9.6692
905	81 90 25	741 217 625	30.0832	9.6727
906	82 08 36	743 677 416	30.0998	9.6763
907	82 26 49	746 142 643	30.1164	9.6799
908	82 44 64	748 613 312	30.1330	9.6834
909	82 62 81	751 089 429	30.1496	9.6870
910	82 81 00	753 571 000	30.1662	9.6905
911	82 99 21	756 058 031	30.1828	9.6941
912	83 17 44	758 550 825	30.1993	9.6976
913	83 35 69	761 048 497	30.2159	9.7012
914	83 53 96	763 551 944	30.2324	9.7047
915	83 72 25	766 060 875	30.2490	9.7082
916	83 90 56	768 575 296	30.2655	9.7118
917	84 08 89	771 095 213	30.2820	9.7153
918	84 27 24	773 620 632	30.2985	9.7188
919	84 45 61	776 151 559	30.3150	9.7224
920	84 64 00	778 688 000	30.3315	9.7259
921	84 82 41	781 229 961	30.3480	9.7294
922	85 00 84	783 777 448	30.3645	9.7329
923	85 19 29	786 330 467	30.3809	9.7364
924	85 37 76	788 889 024	30.3974	9.7400
925	85 56 25	791 453 125	30.4138	9.7435
926	85 74 76	794 022 776	30.4302	9.7470
927	85 93 29	796 597 983	30.4467	9.7505
928	86 11 84	799 178 752	30.4631	9.7540
929	86 30 41	801 765 089	30.4795	9.7575
930	86 49 00	804 357 000	30.4959	9.7610
931	86 67 61	806 954 491	30.5123	9.7645
932	86 86 24	809 557 568	30.5287	9.7680
933	87 04 89	812 166 237	30.5450	9.7715
934	87 23 56	814 780 504	30.5614	9.7750
935	87 42 25	817 400 375	30.5778	9.7785
936	87 60 96	820 025 856	30.5941	9.7819
937	87 79 69	822 656 953	30.6105	9.7854
938	87 98 44	825 293 672	30.6268	9.7889
939	88 17 21	827 936 019	30.6431	9.7924
940	88 36 00	830 584 000	30.6594	9.7959
941	88 54 81	833 237 621	30.6757	9.7993
942	88 73 64	835 896 888	30.6920	9.8028
943	88 92 49	838 561 807	30.7083	9.8063
944	89 11 36	841 232 384	30.7246	9.8097
945	89 30 25	843 908 625	30.7409	9.8132
946	89 49 16	846 590 536	30.7571	9.8167
947	89 68 09	849 278 123	30.7734	9.8201
948	89 87 04	851 971 392	30.7896	9.8236
949	90 06 01	854 670 349	30.8058	9.8270
950	90 25 00	857 375 000	30.8221	9.8305

Number	Square.	Cube.	Square Root.	Cube Root.
951	90 44 01	860 085 351	30.8383	9.8339
952	90 63 04	862 801 408	30.8545	9.8374
953	90 82 09	865 523 177	30.8707	9.8408
954	91 01 16	868 250 664	30.8869	9.8443
955	91 20 25	870 983 875	30.9031	9.8477
956	91 39 36	873 722 816	30.9192	9.8511
957	91 58 49	876 467 493	30.9354	9.8546
958	91 77 64	879 217 912	30.9516	9.8580
959	91 96 81	881 974 079	30.9677	9.8614
960	92 16 00	884 736 000	30.9839	9.8648
961	92 35 21	887 503 681	31.0000	9.8683
962	92 54 44	890 277 128	31.0161	9.8717
963	92 73 69	893 056 347	31.0322	9.8751
964	92 92 96	895 841 344	31.0483	9.8785
965	93 12 25	898 632 125	31.0644	9.8819
966	93 31 56	901 428 696	31.0805	9.8854
967	93 50 89	904 231 063	31.0966	9.8888
968	93 70 24	907 039 232	31.1127	9.8922
969	93 89 61	909 853 209	31.1288	9.8956
970	94 09 00	912 673 000	31.1448	9.8990
971	94 28 41	915 498 611	31.1609	9.9024
972	94 47 84	918 330 048	31.1769	9.9058
973	94 67 29	921 167 317	31.1929	9.9092
974	94 86 76	924 010 424	31.2090	9.9126
975	95 06 25	926 859 375	31.2250	9.9160
976	95 25 76	929 714 176	31.2410	9.9194
977	95 45 29	932 574 833	31.2570	9.9227
978	95 64 84	935 441 352	31.2730	9.9261
979	95 84 41	938 313 739	31.2890	9.9295
980	96 04 00	941 192 000	31.3050	9.9329
981	96 23 61	944 076 141	31.3209	9.9363
982	96 43 24	946 966 168	31.3369	9.9396
983	96 62 89	949 862 087	31.3528	9.9430
984	96 82 56	952 763 904	31.3688	9.9464
985	97 02 25	955 671 625	31.3847	9.9497
986	97 21 96	958 585 256	31.4006	9.9531
987	97 41 69	961 504 803	31.4166	9.9565
988	97 61 44	964 430 272	31.4325	9.9598
989	97 81 21	967 361 669	31.4484	9.9632
990	98 01 00	970 299 000	31.4643	9.9666
991	98 20 81	973 242 271	31.4802	9.9699
992	98 40 64	976 191 488	31.4960	9.9733
993	98 60 49	979 146 657	31.5119	9.9766
994	98 80 36	982 107 784	31.5278	9.9800
995	99 00 25	985 074 875	31.5436	9.9833
996	99 20 16	988 047 936	31.5595	9.9866
997	99 40 09	991 026 973	31.5753	9.9900
998	99 60 04	994 011 992	31.5911	9.9933
999	99 80 01	997 002 999	31.6070	9.9967
1000	1 00 00 00	1 000 000 000	31.6228	10.0000